MW00635563

7 DAYS OF RIDESHARE

by Mayi
Driving through COVID-19, Divorce, and Christianity.

Copyright © 2021 by **Mayi.**

All rights reserved. No part of this publication may be reproduced, distributed or transmitted in any form or by any means, without prior written permission.

Book Layout © 2021 DorronDesigns.com

Book Editing by Emmy Schipani

Published by Lab Coat Writers LLC

7 Days of Rideshare / Mayi.. -- 1st ed.
ISBN 978-0-578-91728-3

TABLE OF CONTENTS

INTRODUCTION

I am Mayi, pronounced as Ma-yee. Everything you are about to read, every conversation, meeting and car ride is true as I experienced it. Nothing has been fabricated, glorified or sensationalized. Names and certain places have been altered to protect identities.

You will read two love stories with two different leading men, Jesus and me. One love flourishes as the other dies. This is a story of addiction, hope and faith. If this journey can shine a light on someone else who is struggling, it is all worth it. Remember no one is perfect and we could all use a second chance. I pray that you enjoy the read.

COVID-19 AND THE WEEKEND WARRIOR

It's Saturday, April 25th, 2020. We are in the middle of a global pandemic brought on by the Wuhan Flu/ Corona Virus/ COVID-19. Whatever you want to call this disease, the U.S. along with the rest of the world is in chaos. My day normally starts at 5 A.M. to hit the power hours in the rideshare business. Since agreeing to file for divorce from my wife right before the pandemic hit, my schedule has been inconsistent. Judging from the intensity of the sunshine pouring in through my white blinds and bouncing off the walls, I will have to work harder today to meet my $200 daily goal. Moving the pillow-shield off my face and grudgingly rolling over onto my side, the glow of the bedside clock flashing 7:11 A.M. meets my eyes.

"Swish, swish," gurgling and spitting, brushing my teeth in the shower, scrubbing my body quickly, my heart pounds with the stress of time and money squeezing in on me. The shower is small, two by three feet in a little rented apartment grabbed hastily for my son and me. My wife and her children now reside in the only home I ever owned. While drying off, outfit ideas rotate through my mind. Unfortunately, most items are in a dirty laundry pile that is growing. Finding my baby blue shirt at the bottom of my near empty third-dresser drawer, leads me to put on my rocking blue Nike Pegasus. My shoes have got to match my outfit, or I feel off, even more off than this divorce has made me. Plopping down into the corner of my L-shaped couch and smacking my lips, shoveling Honey Nut Cheerios down my throat with my last clean spoon, I turn on the TV "Click," knowing it will all be about the virus.

I scroll through my phone and turn the rideshare apps on. While buckling my watch, the news anchorman's report plays on the television, continuing to raise my stress levels. *"COVID-19 also known as the coronavirus disease is caused by the virus SARS-COV-2 per the WHO (World Health Organization). The name was chosen because it is genetically related to the coronavirus responsible for the SARS outbreak in 2003. Coronaviruses have spiky projections on their surface that look like crowns. Corona means crown in Latin."*

Being Latin seems to be the only thing we have in common. He continues, *"Most human corona viruses cause mild respiratory illnesses like the common cold. The origin of both SARS and COVID-19 are believed to be from bats, in this case, passed to civet cats, and then to humans."*

Paying full-attention to the TV screen, eyes wide open, the bottom feed scrolls, *"2.8 million cases worldwide. 202,000 total deaths."* Screenshots flash on the TV of abandoned streets due to the worldwide lockdown. Economies have been halted to a stand-still. Looks like the world has stopped spinning, just like the globe on my desk. The U.S. government has ordered all non-essential businesses to close causing the unemployment rate to skyrocket. Businesses can't afford to keep their employees on anymore. Lately, I feel like I'm the only one on the road. Lower to middle-class Americans, like myself, are feeling it the most. The government thinks $1200 is sufficient for the stimulus package given to tax paying Americans. What a joke! I don't believe the numbers being reported are accurate due to politics, such as stimulus incentives given to hospitals for declaring positive COVID-19 patients. The daily lives of Americans have been changed whether they have COVID-19 or not.

"Click," I change the channel and think, *"They better come up with something quick because in a month South Florida's tri-county area is going to be 100 degrees. It's already hard enough to breathe without the added problem of a "severe acute respiratory syndrome."* This reminds me of the movie, "Contagion." Aware of the dangers and potential health risks I put my family, friends, and body through from driving, leaves me feeling conflicted, but poor people have to work. A lot of my rideshare friends are sitting at home waiting on an unemployment check that hasn't arrived yet, even though they applied more than a month ago. My bills aren't going to take a break, so I have not stopped driving a single day. Due to COVID-19, the rideshare companies require drivers to take extra safety precautions. Sanitizing my 2019 Honda Civic after each ride is a must.

"Click, click," changing the channel, a ride request comes in from Boynton Beach, Florida to the Ft. Lauderdale Airport. After turning off the TV and locking the door behind me, I scamper to my car. Having cleaned it last night, all that is left to do is put on my seatbelt, push the "On" button, and throw the blue sedan into high gear. At 8:15 A.M. my car idles at the pick-up point in an upper-class neighborhood. The trees and hedges are perfectly shaped squares and circles as if trimmed by the best barbers in the shop. All the houses are lined up nice and neat, some even with white picket fences. Suzy stampedes out of the garage yelling at her mother and throws a suitcase full of clothes on the garage floor. I can't make out what she is yelling. She's wearing black skinny jeans, a black tank top, and no shoes. She is blonde with light blue eyes. Suzy is attractive, but frail, dehydrated with a prune face and too skinny, like a toothpick.

She stumbles as she marches over, puts her trembling hands on her hips, and squints her eyes. "You're here way early. What are you doing here? I'm not ready!"

I talk a lot with my hands thanks to my Cuban heritage. With my palms facing down at a 45-degree angle and shaking them back and forth to calm her, I look her in the eye, "Suzy, relax. I move as soon as

I get the job. Can't control if I'm early, but I'm not that kind of driver. Take your time. Get yourself together and make sure you don't forget anything as you're going to the airport. It is Suzy, right?"

"Yes."

"Do you need help with the luggage on the floor?"

She flashes a dimpled smile and walks back to the luggage, "zip," gently replying, "Please." I put her luggage in the trunk. She steps back inside the house to get the rest of her belongings and pops back outside a minute later, continuing to yell at her mother.

"You don't love me! You made me sleep outside with the dog! I love you more. I wouldn't do that to you."

Looking up to the shiny blue sky, I mumble, "Oh boy. This should be interesting. God help me." I open and close the door for her as I do for most customers, "THUMP!" I pull my disposable blue face mask up over my mouth and nostrils, hop in my car, and close my door.

Upon take off, Suzy leans back to dial her phone. "Yeah, twenty, cool, O.K." She hangs up the phone and looks mischievously all around the car. Looks at me. Looks wildly again around the car. Looks back at me, and finally asks, "Can we go to Palm Beach Lakes Blvd. first?"

One side of my lip raises with a silly smirk. "This is your ride. We can go wherever you want. I'll drive you to Tallahassee if you'd like. Is that why you were looking all around? Trying to muster up the courage to ask me?" Her face brightens.

I drive anywhere for my customers. Not to mention we get paid per mile and minute you are in the car. My playlist is playing, "Reckless Love of God." Suzy crosses her arms and rambles on, "Can you believe her? My mother made me sleep outside with the dog on a patio couch because I travel a lot and was worried about the COVID-19. Her own daughter, but I should have expected it, living with that monster. I can't stand my stepdad. He is such an asshole. But that's enough about my family and me. Soooooo anyways, uh...so how long have you been a Christian?"

My cheeks dimple up, "What makes you think I'm a Christian?"
She smiles back, "Well, the music, of course."

The Christian question always brings me back to Saturday, March 10th of 2018. The packed auditorium exploded in excitement, "CLAP, CLAP, CLAP..." Over 1,000 stood up as the first person walked to the church stage that cool Ft. Lauderdale night and made his way to Pastor DS. Nervous, full of adrenaline and butterflies, not just in my stomach, but even in my heart, I made my bold approach. Ironically, I was dressed in all black that day – jeans, shirt, leather jacket, and shoes, yet it was the day my soul was brought into the Light. Pastor DS doesn't know it, but the way he explains the Gospel and Jesus is part of the reason I chose to save my life that night and accept Jesus as my Lord and Savior. Elevated at the balls of my feet and lifting myself over the stage, as other people were arriving to change their lives, my wife leaned closer to my 5'7, 170-pound frame and whispered, "I'm very proud of you Papi."

Nodding up and down a tidal wave gushes from my eyes. "I know. I love you."

Pastor DS continues, "You're repeating after me but, when you choose to repeat it, you're accepting and receiving Jesus Christ into your heart. You are professing with your own mouth."

I repeated, "Jesus, I am a sinner. I believe that you died for my sins. I believe that you are my Lord and Savior. I ask you to come into my heart and wash me of my sins. Come into my heart, and I will walk with you for the rest of my days. In the name of Jesus Christ, I pray, Amen!" My wife and I hugged and followed the crowd into the meeting room. I was not sure exactly what to expect.

Leaving the meeting room feeling like a brand-new man who was head over heels for his wife, kids, and the Lord, I was inspired. The family I had been desperately seeking, the reason for living, was finally here with me.

Thoughts of the divorce interrupt the euphoric memory. I snap back to the present. "Suzy, I was saved in March of 2018 but, it really took a hold of me last month."

Suzy has already moved on to the next topic. "It says here you have been driving for over two years. Oh, you're from Boca. A Boca boy. Can I take this mask off?"

Chuckling, shaking my head up and down I reply, "You can take yours off if I can take mine off."

She pulls her mask off. "Thank you."

Pulling my mask down and rubbing the little mask hairs off my chin, I share my story. "Thank you, and technically, yes. I was born in Cuba. Came over when I was three years old. I have been here for thirty-nine years and grew up in Boca for twenty-eight years. Greatest city. Hidden gem. I love Jesus but, we are not supposed to be talkin' religion. Sorry to hear about you having to sleep outside last night but it is kind of funny. Hey, didn't it rain last night?" I look back in the rearview mirror at Suzy.

"Yes, it did but, I got lucky. It only rained here for ten minutes. I still got a little wet. That's why I wasn't ready this morning and became so upset. I'm still a little fucking wet!" She exclaims. We both laugh, our voices fading into the background of the music playing. We pull off on the Palm Beach Lakes exit ramp to the Marathon Gas station on the south side immediately off I-95.

"I definitely believe in God. I'll be right back." She jumps out of my car and rushes into an old car parked a few spots over. She busts out of that car and back into mine a few minutes later, "O.K. Ready. Let's go!"

Pulling out of the lot, I squint my eyes, purse my lips, look in the rearview mirror and ask, "Ok, so what drugs did we just buy?"

Acting dazed and puzzled, she replies, "Hard!"

Biting my cheek, I blink, "What is hard?"

She replies, "Crack!"

"Aaaah, interesting. So, what are you going to do? You gonna' eat it, sniff it, what?"

She squeals like a five-year-old child asking for ice cream. "I was hoping you would let me smoke it."

My eyes pop out, and my voice raises. "There's no way in hell you're going to smoke that crap in my car."

She rummages through her carry-on, looking deep down into it. "Come on, man. I'm on my way to the fucking airport to turn myself into rehab. No one is fucking making me. I choose to turn myself in." Suzy looks back up at me with glossy eyes and a desperate stare. *"Please let me get high. Please let me get my last high in?"*

Looking straight at the roadway ahead, I grip the steering wheel a little tighter. We sit in silence with the Christian music playing. Hopping on I-95 South, my eyes wander everywhere. Up, left, right, the cars, the highway. Staring ahead again, counting the yellow lines with a stern look on my face, I think, *"Is this real or a story to get high before getting on the plane?"*

Conflicted with morality, rideshare guidelines, federal laws, and my Christianity, I find it a difficult decision and hope to do the right thing. I know what she needs is to quit. I hear what she wants and feel sorry for her. Do I choose to follow my moral high road versus showing compassion for another human being struggling? Do I let her get high in my car? Suzy speaks up with a wide grin. "If you let me smoke it, I'll let you keep the ride on and take it back home."

Money can sometimes make us forget who we are, who we are trying to be, and where we are trying to go. I have done some stupid things for money and have put myself in harm's way in the past. I couldn't believe I was about to do it again. I smile, look in the rear-view mirror and say, "Let me get this straight. If I let you smoke it, I can keep the ride on, drive home, and get paid?"

She beams, "Yes!"

My past makes me empathize with her. Plus, this would be the only ride I'd have to do today. I look into the rearview mirror with my eyes downcast a bit, beaten. "Yes, you can smoke your crack but, if we get pulled over, I don't know shit. I'll tell the officer that I don't look back at my customers because my eyes are on the road and that I thought it was a vape that you were smoking back there."

She agrees. "Ok, we have a deal. I was going to let you take the ride back anyway because I was going to ask you to return my mom's keys. I forgot to leave them."

With a frown, I mutter, "Wonderful."

She lays back, packs a tiny clear pipe and lights up, "pfff, pfff."

Before you judge me, remember I am human. I make mistakes, a lot of them. I am a sinner but, try my hardest to be pure. Every night I get on my knees and pray for forgiveness, understanding, and mercy. Sometimes my choices are made out of sheer boredom or for the unique experience. Normally, my spirit wins the war. Sometimes, my flesh and brain win a battle or two. This was no longer a normal world. Seeing humans at all had become a rarity other than when driving. People were too afraid to go out and if you did, you stayed six feet apart per CDC recommendation. Maybe part of me was just lonely.

We are on I-95 heading south, "Oceans, where feet may fail," is playing. Sweat drips down my forehead and the ride is spent looking both ways frantically to be sure there are no cops swooping in on the scene. "Whoosh, whoosh," the wind howls with the windows half-cracked. I make every effort to breathe through my mouth, refusing to breathe the stench of this burning toxin through my nose. I don't even know how to compare the smell. Maybe nasty burning sulfur or the smell of Styrofoam burnt in a microwave. The mixture of burning crack and muggy South Florida humidity is choking me. I'm looking for that precious I-595 East sign amongst the warehouses and countless billboards lining the highway. She sinks back further into the seat, letting out a huge breath, and says, "Let me tell you why I believe in God."

"Go for it. I'm interested in hearing this," and turn down the volume on the radio.

Her eyes fill with tears. Her voice cracks, "I was twenty-two and on the back of my boyfriend's motorcycle. He got into a situation and he had to make a maneuver. During this lane change, he hit the rear side of a fucking box truck. I went flying off the fucking bike into the back of the box truck. Paralyzed from the waist down, the doctors said I would never fucking walk again. I told them I would walk again. Shitheads. My boyfriend fucking kills himself a year later. It was hard on me. I prayed, and I prayed, and I prayed. It wasn't until I started praying that the physical therapy started to work. I'm walking again, and that's why I believe in God. I believe he had his hand in getting my life back."

"Wow! That's crazy. That is fucking nuts and awesome that you're walking." I reply, merging onto I-595 East for our final approach to the airport. We can hear the sound barrier break around us continuously.

Arriving at the airport in harried state with dilated eyes she says, "I wish you hadn't met me like this. I wasn't always like this. I was sober for four years and relapsed eighteen days ago. Hey, you think you can park and make sure I check my luggage and myself in O.K?"

I nod, "O.K. I was going to suggest that anyways. You look... fucked up!" We burst with unrestrained laughter. After parking my car, we stroll into the airport with her worn red suitcase bumping along, able to see clearly from one end to the other without any crowds to look over. I could hear our footsteps echoing. I am three paces behind her when something drops out of a hole in her back pocket, "CRACK!" Something clear falls and shatters, shards landing on the hard floor. She turns over her right shoulder, looks at the debris briefly, and keeps walking with an increased gait. I hesitate for one instant and look at the shattered glass with trepidation. Luckily, we are in the middle of a COVID-19 crisis, and there is absolutely no one in the airport to witness the mess. I catch up to her at baggage check-in and whisper, "Is that what I think it was? You are fucking lucky it's not a normal day at this airport."

She whispers back, "OMG. I totally fucking forgot that was in there."

I say with a grin, "That's a good thing, then I guess. You're so high, you probably would have gotten busted."

She asks, "Can I have your number in case anything out of the ordinary happens?"

"I'm not sure what can happen. You have forty minutes, and there's no one here." I write my number on her baggage claim ticket, exit the sliding glass doors, and return to my car. I look at my phone to verify the rideshare app is still running and start to drive home like we agreed.

On the way back, the windows remain at half-staff. Fresh breeze blows on my face. The evil crack stench lingers. Heading north on I-95, halfway home, my phone rings. It reads "unknown number." I pick up, and it's exactly who I thought it would be. Suzy takes a deep breath. "Turn around. Come get me. I didn't make the flight. I'll explain later."

Still getting paid for the same ride, I turn the car around thinking the whole ride back to the airport, *"What could have possibly happened?"*

Suzy is bouncing with energy under Terminal 3 upon arrival. "They wouldn't let me board the plane. They said boarding was over early for some reason and they still wanted me to go through TSA security. I asked why would I go through TSA security if I can't even board the plane? I swear they saw me drop the pipe, and they wanted me to go through the checkpoint so they can fucking snatch me."

"Suzy, I doubt they can snatch you if you don't have anything on you. So, your luggage left?"

"Yeah."

"So, what's the plan? Where are we going? What are we doing?"

"Well, I was able to change my flight for a 3 P.M. flight today but, I don't know what to do. I don't have anywhere to go. I don't have any real money. My luggage is on the way to California. What a fucking mess."

"Back to your mom's?"

She laughs, "Yeah, for the keys. She's probably going to be fucking pissed I missed the flight, but I can't go back there to wait for the flight."

After five minutes of silence and some hard thought, I say, "I'm going to do you a solid. We can deliver the keys to your mom. Then, we can go back to my place. I'll get paid all the way there. You look like you could use some rest and a shower."

She asks, "I can go back to your place and wait until the next flight? This does not have anything to do with any sexual favors?"

Arching my brow and recoiling in disgust, I answer. "Are you fucking serious? People do things for other people for sexual favors? I have no such intention, nor do I want to do anything with you. You got the wrong guy, man. I see someone who can use some help, and my heart goes out to you. I think of my sister and mom and how I'd want someone to help them if they were ever in a bind. I simply want to help you. If it makes you feel any better, I'll be the one getting your ride anyway. The rideshare systems are set up for the ride to go to the closest driver logged on."

She wiggles around in the backseat, sighs, and says, "What have I done for God to bring you my way today? I totally needed someone like you today." I don't really think she's playing me but don't want to be naive.

On the way to her mother's, I'm thinking, *"How do you mix crack and God?"* I don't say anything because I don't want to say the wrong thing and turn her off or away from God. So, I just listen. Sometimes that's all people need.

She continues, "My mother would use, and I would take care of her. On my 16th fucking birthday, I used coke for the first fucking time, and it was with my mom. She became more of a friend than a mom. I'm pretty sure she will be upset I didn't get on that plane. I'm not sure we should tell her I'm in the car. What do you think? Should we tell her?"

Sitting outside her mom's house, I say, "I don't know man. I'll do whatever you need. Just tell me how you want to handle this." Suzy shoves a scribbled note, the keys, and four blue pills.

She points at the blue pills, "Only give this Adderall to my mom. Not to anyone else. Just my mom and screw it. If they ask, tell them I'm fucking here."

"O.K."

Her stepdad answers the door on the fourth knock. Imagine the short "Monopoly" Banker but, with brownish curly short hair where a top hat should be. His mustache curls up at the ends, and he has a perfectly round potbelly. I say, "Sir, your stepdaughter asked me to hand this to you," and hand him the tattered yellow paper.

Confused, he blurts, "Huh?"

I repeat, "Your stepdaughter wanted me to hand this to you."

Heading back to my car, Suzy quizzically watches me from the car window. "Your stepdad answered the door, so I only handed him the note."

"Fuck it. Go back and give the keys and the pills to either of them. I don't care anymore."

"Ooooook." I turn on my heels and head back.

Her stepdad answers the door again in a huff. "I'm sorry sir. I forgot she also wanted me to give you these."

He accepts the keys and pills, shoving them in his pocket without looking at them and asks, "Is she in the car?"

"Yes sir."

He raises his voice and with a crimson face snarls, "When you leave here, take her straight to the fucking police. She is not welcome here. You tell her she is not fucking welcome here!"

Backpedaling I mumble, "Yes sir."

After hopping into the car, I turn around in the driver's seat to speak to Suzy. "Nope. You definitely can't go back there. He told me to take you to the fucking cops. What a prick. You don't have to go back there, and I don't have to take you to the cops either. We all have our issues and I'm sure he's just upset because he probably thinks you're fucking high, which you are." I smile. "That's not a good situation. Let's roll. You ready? We good?"

Suzy nods in affirmation. Popping it into gear, we head out. She pinches her lips, looks down, and rumbles through her bag, tossing makeup, hand sanitizer, papers, and change. "No. He fucking hates me. He's such an asshole." Suzy finds and applies her lip gloss in a quick swoop. She keeps rumbling through her bag, and continues, "I don't blame him. It's kind of my mom's fucking fault. He used to find my mom's shit around the house, and she would blame it on me. What am I gonna do, you know? It's my fucking mom."

"I feel ya. We don't get to pick them, and we only get one so, I feel ya." I reply sympathizing.

We arrive at my humble apartment consisting of two suites with a shared bathroom and kitchen in the center. The old Palm Beach Community College dorms now pose as rentals for bachelors and divorcees like me. Can't beat rent, water, power, cable, and internet for less than eleven hundred in South Florida.

We walk into my living/ dining/ bedroom. I drop my keys atop my gray wooden dresser, not caring about the scratches. "Click," I turn on the 55-inch Smart TV. The Samsung is one of the few things I did not leave behind at my old home. Immediately next to the dresser is my closet. It took me forty-two years to finally have my own closet. Standing on the cold beige 18x18 tile and searching around in my closet, I grab the last pair of clean pants off a hanger. "Here. You can wear these Adidas pants." I hand her a matching blue hoodie from the bottom right dresser drawer and a pair of socks from the top drawer. "The hoodie and socks are in case you get cold because that A.C. does not go past sixty-eight. If you're still cold, you can use that checkered blanket on the couch. Towels are in the bathroom. Make yourself at home and help yourself to whatever is in the fridge. It's eleven-thirty, and we have to be back on the road for a 3 P.M. flight. I need to rest. We have been at it since eight." I fall back on my couch and raise the volume to provide my version of white noise.

She walks to the bathroom door with clothes in-hand, "I'm gonna go shower. Thanks for the clothes. I totally appreciate it." After about twenty minutes, Suzy darts out of the bathroom, her hair still wet, in my comfy clothes. She grabs a hairbrush from her "Mary Poppins" bag. She sits next to me, stroking her brush roughly through her tangled hair with one hand.

I ask, "Feels good to be clean, doesn't it? Nice and fresh. Put on whatever show you want to watch, and you can keep those clothes. Those are my favorite pants. I have a feeling they will be yours, too, at the rehab." She sits with her legs crisscrossed style on the couch angled toward me. Her brushing pauses for a moment.

Her eyebrows come together in the middle, "I can't believe you're being this fucking nice to me. Come on. What is it that you really fucking want? What are you going to ask me to do? No one is this fucking nice for no reason."

Sitting up I exclaim, "You're right! I want that fucking ride." Grinning ear to ear, "Why must I want something in return? Granted, I am getting the paid ride, but I thought instead of putting you out on the street, I'd help you out. This is just about helping another human being. Someone was gonna get that ride. May as well be me."

She digs through her bag and produces her cell phone. "Get your phone. I'm about to set up the ride."

A ping from rideshare comes in on my phone. "O.K. Got it. Scheduled. Awesome!"

She looks up at me. "Can you play some of your Gospel music? I love Christian music. It just makes me feel good." Casting my playlist from my phone to the TV, "Joy" plays. She continues, "You have some really good music. Thank you for being nice to me."

"Really, it's no big deal." I reply.

"No, really it fucking is. I haven't had the best of luck with guys. I was on the back of my friend's bike, and we pulled out of his driveway. His girlfriend, that I didn't know he had, must have been watching the house and followed us. She rams the back of the bike and I fly off the back landing on the street. Her friend comes out of the passenger side with two switch blades and starts fucking attacking me. Slices me all the fuck up."

The stone-cold look on my face says it all. Sitting up and trying to process her story, I blurt out, "Well if you knew he had a girlfriend or not is irrelevant. No human being should be able to do this to another. That's fucking crazy. I don't want to sound insensitive but, you're sure you're not bullshitting me?"

Holding tears back, Suzy raises her arms and struggles to get the words out. "You see these?" She pulls at the hoodie to show her bare back, moves her hair aside, turns her neck, and forces out, "You fucking see these?" I feel like a jerk right now, staring at angry scars from her neck to her torso. She grabs my laptop off the coffee table, begins typing away, and says, "If a sweet old couple driving by didn't pick me up and take me to the emergency room, I would have died, bleeding the fuck out while waiting on an ambulance." She clicks on the article with a picture of the crime scene.

Shocked, I ask, "Well, what about the guy driving the fucking bike? Did he at least come back for you or something?"

"No! He didn't have a license for that fucking thing. He just kept going."

"Wow! That's fucked up. Maybe you should stay off bikes. You seem to have bad luck on them." We share a sarcastic smile.

Tapping my watch, "Time to go. Don't want to be late." She gathers her damp clothing off the bathroom floor shoving it inside her bottomless bag. Grabbing a water bottle from underneath my little coffee table we rush out to catch the flight. On cue, as soon as we make the first turn, she says, "Can we stop by a friend's house? I want to say goodbye before I go. It's on the way, and you get paid on the ride for it."

"Sure. I don't see why not, but you have to make it quick, or we won't make this flight." At her friend's house, in a little run-down neighborhood, weeds are growing out of the sidewalk. There is dirt where there should be green grass. There are half hazard rocks thrown about instead of mulch in front of the homes.

"Wait here. I'll be right back," she says. I look at my watch for the time. Fiddling my thumbs, I grab my phone and check out my Crypto accounts. My head is on a swivel looking around this beat-up neighborhood to make sure I don't get jacked. Suzy strolls back into my car, like nothing ever happened, with glossy bloodshot eyes.

Huffing and puffing under my gritted teeth, "I can't believe you just went in there and left me in my car for over thirty minutes so you can get fucking high again. You're lucky I'm getting fucking paid for this time. God, you're like a fucking kid. I bet you even scored more drugs. We will never make it for this flight now."

As nice and sweet as an addict can be, an addict is an addict.

Flailing all over the backseat she cries, "I'm sorry. Can we please try and make it? I have nowhere to go. I have to make this fucking flight." I peel out of the area as quickly as possible.

"I'm going to go, but I can assure you we are not making this flight." I'm weaving and bobbing, ducking and dodging. Looking for the holes ahead of me between cars reminds me of my old running back days. We go through the motions and obviously make it to Ft. Lauderdale in time to miss departure, turn right around, and head back to my apartment.

Still getting paid on the drive back, it's 3:30 P.M, and I've been with Suzy since 8 A.M. "You were never going to make that fucking flight, were you? I bet you even scored enough to last you all day. I'm pretty analytical because of my previous jobs. I'm not a fucking dummy!"

Watching her in the rearview mirror, her cheeks raise, and she forms a mischievous smile. "Man, you're fucking good. Look, like I said. I'm going to turn myself into rehab. No one is making me. Not a fucking judge. Not a fucking charge. Not my fucking parents. Me! That's at least sixty days in a fucking facility. I just met you, and I think you're cool and sweet and would like to just have someone to fucking talk to. I enjoy talking to you. I think you're really kind. Why should I have to turn myself in today, when I can tomorrow? It's fucking Saturday! I have enough dope to last me the day. Can we just chill until tomorrow?"

Sucking my lips inward and looking straight ahead at the highway, thoughts weigh heavy on me. *"O.K. she hasn't lied to you. She seems sweet and just lost. She has nowhere to go and being with me is the safest place."* I look in the mirror and utter, "Ok, we can go back to my place. I don't have my kid this weekend. But if I'm going to have to watch you smoke dope, I have to get some weed."

She yells, "O.K. Let's go!" We make a quick stop where I like to call my southern hub, Ricky Smalls place. He's one of my closest friends and connects. Trust him entirely. Very successful businessman.

The dynamics of the day have changed as much as the Florida weather. Arriving at my apartment, we get caught up in a light drizzle. Suzy runs through the rain drops to get inside and light her pipe. I've never seen someone smoke dope before today. Even weirder was her smoking it and talking about God and Jesus. Suzy sits on my couch and packs her pipe. "Can you play some more of your music?"

"Absolutely." I say sitting next to her on the couch. Casting my phone to the TV, we listen to the soothing sounds of "Open Heaven."

She hits her pipe again and as smoke swirls around her face she says, "The music soothes me. It calms me down from the paranoia. I wish you didn't meet me in this condition. I'm not really like this."

Nodding my head, I lick the top of my blunt and roll it nice. Not too tight; not too loose.

The guilt of lighting up hits me, but I puff away anyway and say, "We all have our things. We all have our fucking demons that we fight. Have a few myself. Don't feel bad. Remember, it's never as good as they say it is, and it's never as bad as they say it is. Everyone's got something." I puff the blunt again and lie back relaxed.

Suzy follows me and says, "Let me tell you why I'm going to rehab..." She says she can't go into much detail as it is an open investigation. Suzy dials a detective and puts her phone on speaker, determined to prove she is being honest with me. She fiddles with her hair, splaying across the couch while the phone rings. The detective doesn't pick up and she leaves him a message.

I immediately get up and pivot from the couch to a chair, swiftly pulling it out from under my table. "I'm sorry, Suzy. I had to get away from that smell."

She sits up, looks down shyly, and then makes eye contact with me. "Remember I mentioned I relapsed eighteen days ago. Well... the day before I relapsed, someone came knocking on my fucking door. I remember saying what does this motherfucker want? I open the door with the chain link locked still, but somehow the door opens inward anyway. He or they, I'm not sure, the cops think it may have been more than one person, bust down the door! So, I think I know who it was but, I was knocked out, so who can be sure? Ya know. I have a blank and can't remember. I wish I could. I'd turn that motherfucker, or fuckers, in." Her lips draw down into a frown of disgust; her face reddens as she holds back tears. "Anyways, when I come to, I'm drenched in water and fucking bleach because he or maybe they, raped me." Despite her best efforts the tears fall. She wipes off her cheeks. Dropping her hands in defeat she says, "They took a razor and fucking slit me like a fish. What kind of fucking bastard does that? Like it wasn't bad enough to fucking rape me, right?" She continues to wipe her face.

Taken aback, I say "What a sick animal to do something like that. I'm so sorry."

She says, "That's why I asked about the sexual favor. That's the last fucking thing I'm thinking about. Not that you're not good looking. I just, you know..."

I interrupt, "It's cool, man. I get it. Not what I had in mind anyway, so it's cool, and I would never."

The rest of the evening, she sits on the couch and listens to music, relaxing as we get to know one another. I sit at the table, keeping my distance. She is into the Patriots and baseball, so I walk into my closet and pull out an old shoe box and open the lid to reveal a mint condition football card. "Look, check out my Tom Brady autographed rookie card. I bought it for 1k the day before the Super Bowl, and after beating the Rams it was worth 3K. Here are some of my baseball articles. I played for twelve years, year-round. Went to college on a full ride for baseball and an academic scholarship. Best fucking times of my life."

We talk some more. She cries and wipes her face continuously. Then I give her some words of encouragement. Moving to the couch I grab her hands and look into her eyes, "Don't you think there's more for you than smoking dope and fucking doing drugs? You are a strong woman. Do you know most people don't survive one of these traumatic experiences? Some get depressed and kill themselves. You have not only survived one traumatic experience, but three. I actually believe that, since you were sixteen years old, your life has been one huge fucking traumatic experience. If you can get cleaned up, you have a story to tell. You can inspire not just women but numerous people. You have to get cleaned up first." Her face is puffy from all the crying. "If you get cleaned up, you start getting credibility. Without getting cleaned up, you have no credibility. I'll be more than willing to help you. We can start a channel for you. I think you could help a lot of fucking people." More tears escape, and she gives me a hug.

I hand her a tissue from the box on my white computer desk and ask, "What time is the flight tomorrow?"

Blowing her nose loudly I hear her say, "6 A.M." through her sniffles.

Exasperated, I exclaim, "Why in the hell would you make a flight for 6 A.M. when you know you can't make a fucking 8 A.M?" Suzy shrugs her shoulders in confusion.

Dusk turns to night and I yawn. "It's late and we gotta get up early tomorrow. I'm sleeping here on the couch and you can sleep on the bed."

Suzy's face blushes, her voice lowers, "Can you sleep on the bed with me? I trust you. I don't think you will try anything, and I could use the affection." We get off the couch, turn off the TV and shut off the lights. I lay with her and scratch her back until she gives into the night. I leave the bed, set an alarm on my phone, and go back on the couch to sleep.

"ERR...ERR...ERR!" My 4 A.M. alarm blasts, and I muscle out of the couch. After making my way to the bedroom nightstand I slam my hand down on the alarm clock to shut it off and begin tapping Suzy, "Hey, wake up. Wake up. We gotta get ready to go."

"Wa? What? Let me sleep." She mumbles rolling over and raising the covers above her head.

Tenderly tapping her again I beg, "Suzy, come on. I let you sleep as long as you can. You can sleep in my car. We gotta go."

As slow as a snail, she gets up off the bed and stomps into the bathroom. I sit on my couch while waiting and rest. Suzy steps out of the bathroom and asks, "Can we go to my friend's house, please?"

Crossing my arms, my answer is firm. "No, Suzy. If we do, we won't make that flight."

"I don't fuckin' care. There is another flight I would rather take. I already checked on it."

My right-hand rubs my stubbled chin. I shake my head left and right. "Wow! You seem to have all the fucking answers. If I do this, we are going through the same motions again all the way to the airport and back while I get paid. I'm not really comfortable doing this shit... again!"

Suzy dials her phone while I brush my teeth. "My friend isn't picking up, but I got a spot we can go to on the way."

Once I finish brushing my teeth, I snatch my keys from the table. "Let's ride!" We hurry through the drizzle avoiding the little puddles and zoom into the car. My wipers are new, so my view is clear but dark. My speed is cautious. Traveling West Atlantic Blvd in Pompano, more than halfway to the airport, Suzy grumbles, "Turn off the A.C. please."

"Yes, Ma'am."

"Make a right at the next street and then the following right."

"Got it." I turn the corner only to see run-down homes and multiple dead ducks on the ground. Trash covers the sidewalks spilling out of garbage cans into the pot-holed streets.

She says, "Go around the next corner and park. One of these guys is going to come up to the window and then we can leave." There are four guys on the corner, and my head is on a swivel. I'm locked in, looking around to make sure we don't get killed.

I park at the corner and caution Suzy. "If this gets shady, I'm taking off. I don't care if I fuckin' run someone over."

A gangly guy in jeans and a beat up undershirt with yellow stains under the armpits saunters over to the rear passenger window on my side. Suzy slides over and rolls down the window. "Yo, what's up? Here is your $10. Thanks. Let's go." We go through the motions again and head back to my place. The water and wind are crashing against my car, "WOOOSH...wooosh...wooosh!" The wind howls and screams. In no rush at all, knowing we have no shot at making the flight, we find ourselves back at my place once more. I pull up a chair and place it in front of her, sitting face to face.

My voice deepens. "Suzy, I know what you and your body are going through. The only reason I agreed to this fucking crazy weekend is that I've been there, where you are. Not as bad, but I've fucking been there, and I wish I had someone at that time. Also, because I knew you'd be turning yourself in. I was letting you have a place of sanctuary and peace that I know you needed. Not to mention this was going to be the safest place for you. I had three fucking DUI's, was heavily on drugs and drinking, and thought my life was over. Luckily, having my son at thirty, and Jesus Christ saved my life. Now, you have my number and I want to make this clear." I grab her hands. "Go get cleaned up. When you come back, if you need or want my help, I will be here. However, I will not condone, tolerate, or enable this behavior with me again. I will not be making any fucking drug runs no matter how much money I'm offered. I will not let you get high here. I have a kid, a life, and I'm not willing to risk it again. I did this time because I wanted to try and help you. I will not assist you in drug runs again. I hope I'm fucking clear."

"Crystal, no pun intended. I totally appreciate everything you have done for me this weekend. It's more than anyone could have expected." I move my chair back to the table and sit. She pulls out the little bit of dope she has and packs it in the clear pipe. Leans back. "Ppfff, Ppfff, Want some?"

"No thanks. I'm good with my weed."

She frowns and sits back up. "I'm sorry. I shouldn't have done that. I know better."

Chuckling to myself and breaking up the flower, I turn and look at Suzy, turn back and finish rolling one up to pass the time. "It's O.K. No one is going to make me do anything I don't want, especially a chick." She offers it to me again and I decline. I've never tried it and see no need.

She blushingly declares, "I think I'm going to wear the outfit you gave me."

"Do that. I'm going to take a nap. We have six hours before we have to leave." I cast my music to the TV and lay on my couch. Suzy runs into the bathroom and changes. The pot settles me into a deep sleep.

We leave super early because of the rain, and get to Fort Lauderdale airport by 3 P.M. It is a very quiet trip. We are one and a half hours early. No way she misses this flight. Suzy's eyes are bloodshot and strung out with big black circles. She is in the back seat complaining as I pull up to the terminal. "I can't believe I'm turning myself in today. I don't want to, but I know I fuckin' need to."

I supportively exclaim, "You will be fine!" No parking, leaving nothing to chance, I leave the ignition on, get out, and meet her on the passenger side of the Civic insisting, "Call me when you get to Texas, so I know you're safe. Have a safe and smooth flight."

She gives me a hug and an uninvited peck on the lips, catching me off guard. "Thank you," she whispers.

"You're welcome. Get cleaned up." I hug her again and then jump back in the car. Pulling away and looking back to make sure there is no oncoming traffic, I notice a note in the back.

It reads as follows:

"Never have I given a coin away 'cause they are the hardest things I've ever had to do. Until yesterday death was around me. I wanted to leave hell and meet my keeper. Then I met you. Consider me in your success of saving lives 'cause you saved mine. I'm not a coin but I hope to be as important as one."

I'm not so sure I did save her life. Honestly, as much as I'd like to take any credit, it's not mine to take. It's Jesus, the man upstairs. He inspired some major changes in me. Driving home, questions linger, *"He's the one who saved her life just like He did mine. I'm also not so sure I helped much, or that I'm that good of a guy. I still let her do drugs. Would I have helped a fellow man that was a crack head? Would I have felt comfortable? Would I have felt threatened? Would I have done it without getting the paid rides?"*

Sunday night, upon landing in Texas she sent me selfies of her standing in the airport alone. She called me the next day as she sat in a rideshare, supposedly in the Lone Star State, *"Hey! Can you send me twenty bucks so I can get something to eat?"*

That could be true, and if she had made it to California, where her rehab was located, I might have sent her the money, but instead I said, "No ma'am. I know where it may, and probably will, go. Thank you for your note. It was touching. Now get your butt to rehab." Naturally, she got mad, and I had not heard from her since.

This is one of the craziest rides I've ever done. However, I had a chance to help another human being and make some money at the same time. Ended up completing four rides that weekend for over four hundred dollars. One hundred and change each round trip with a little volunteer babysitting. Not the worst ride ever. No! For that, we have to go back to when I started driving part-time about two years ago. For me, that was the scariest and most threatening ride I feel I have ever completed. I had just come to know Christ...

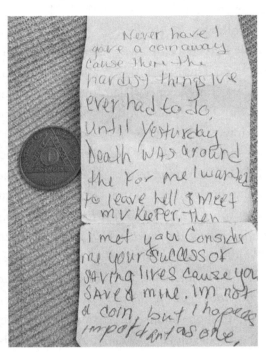

*Note left in my backseat.

WORST RIDE EVER!

By Easter weekend 2018, my decision to get baptized was final. The church held a public baptism at Pompano Beach. There I was along with my wife and extended family. I ran into an old friend from Boca High. His dad was getting baptized, too. One thing about the Tri-county area is you never know who you will run into.

Approaching the shoreline, we taste the salt whipping through the air. The palm trees shiver back and forth as if they also forgot to bring a jacket. Despite the cold water, my heart kept me warm.

"I got it, babe!" Yelling and waving my wife off with one hand; catching her hat with the other. My flip flops spray piles of sand into the air like rounds off a machine gun. "Try holding it down so it doesn't fly off again."

"Thank you, Papi. We are meeting my parents at the red flag by the water."

The sandpaper between my toes is rough as we march toward her parents. "Hey, guys, how are you?" I give her Dad, Antonio a hug and wave to her Mom.

Embracing his daughter, Antonio says, "We are good. Just here for your moment. You almost ready? It's cold out here."

"Yes sir. I'm cold, too. Let's get this show on the road." We turn and trudge through the sand once again until we arrive to witness the pastors dipping people one by one into the water.

A pastor with blond wavy hair, standing in the ocean wet to his knees, suddenly glances my way mid-dip, "Mayi?"

"Dan? You're a pastor here?"

"Yes, I am."

I turn to my family. "Guys, this is Dan. I went to Boca High with Dan. Dan; this is my wife and her parents." They shake hands and acquaint themselves.

"So, Dan…You dippin' me?"

"Yes sir! Cool, right?"

"Yeah, man. That's awesome!"

"You ready to go?"

"Absolutely!" Giving my wife a quick hug and a kiss, I follow Dan into the water and become sandwiched in between Dan and the other pastor.

We bow our heads to say a quick prayer. "Heavenly Father, we ask that you clean Mayi of his sins and accept him into your Kingdom."

"Amen!" They dip me and I explode up out of the cold water. Exiting a minute later, shivering, and confused by the fact that I don't immediately feel different, questions swirl in my mind, *Am I a bad person? Did I not receive the Holy Spirit? Maybe, I'm not supposed to feel different? Maybe, I'm just supposed to feel better. A boost. A kickstart in the right direction."* I know one thing. I was where I was supposed to be. It was divine intervention leading me to encounter two good friends at the baptism.

Throwing a towel around me at the shoreline, Dan asks, "How do you feel? You feel different?"

"I feel better. I guess I feel different. Definitely better."

"Ah, don't worry about it, man. It will come. I know your heart, Mayi."

I can hear my family asking the same question a few feet away. All looking at me for an answer.

"Do you feel any different Mayi?"

"I feel better. I feel cleansed. I wanted to do this for Jesus and myself. I wanted to profess that He is my Lord and Savior. Guys, it's cold, and I'm wet. Let's get out of here."

Antonio raises his hands to wave, shouting excitedly, "Let's go have lunch and celebrate!"

"Thank you all for coming. It means a lot to me. Let's go eat. I'm starving. Antonio, let's go to your favorite place, the Olive Garden."

"Mmmmm…Mayi I'll never turn that down. Even Jesus supplied unlimited breadsticks."

The following week was spent seeking answers, asking people about the Holy Spirit and Jesus. I was hungry for answers and kept asking my wife, her dad, and Dan questions about how they felt when they were baptized. I was getting parables from them and doing my own research. Before you knew it, Sunday was here.

I rolled over, slipping my hands slowly under my wife's nightgown and caressing her petite frame. She is a gorgeous Venezuelan trophy wife. Spanish soap opera "Novella" type. Her bright auburn hair contrasts with her pale pinkish skin, and freckled face. Her light eyes brighten up any room. Her smile is infectious when it appears, which lately was not as often.

Feeling her round, perky breasts and dimples on the back of her shoulders, I realize she is perfectly pink. Great woman inside as well. One drink, and she was nice and tipsy. A non-tobacco smoker, which was a must for me.

She lent me the impression she was a caring mother and stepmother. She worked part-time as a Licensed Massage Therapist in Royal Palm Beach. We enjoyed spending time together, especially working out in the gym. She didn't really go out and drank sparingly, at least at the beginning of our marriage. Thankfully she loved Christ and me.

Sliding my arms downward, caressing her thighs, I begin calling her pet name from our courting days. "Tinderella, wake up Tinderella."

"Ahh, Mmm…Mmmmm, Ahh my Tinderoni." She starts to moan. "Right there, right there Papi." We speak the same love language. Our bodies move in unison while making love, like the waves of the ocean crashing on the shore with force and the sand giving way. A red-hot lava lamp swirling in tandem and conforming to its surrounding. My body makes its way into missionary position, just the way she likes it. My lips smooch her wet, soft lips over and over.

"I love the way you just give me your body. You are so yummy baby!" I say with excitement as I thrust. I make her feel comfortable in her skin, loving every inch of her. I hold her close, grab her waist and flip her over quickly, so she can be on top.

"Aaaaah, mmm, Uh, Uh, PAPI!" She roars in ecstasy while we look deep into each other's eyes.

"Slap. Clap. Slap. Clap." Repetitively our hips and thighs collide harder and faster, harder and faster, over and over until we move as one.

"Aaa...Mmmm...Aaa...Mmm." I gently throw her onto her side and mount her deeply with the carnal speed of 100 pumas chasing 100 cougars. Playfully pulling her long hair with one hand and spanking her perfect round butt cheek with the other to the rhythm of our thighs clapping, I slow down and tease, "You like that baby?"

She clutches the sheets with both hands and roars. "Uh huh, Aaahhh! I love everything you do to me Papi!" We both finish and fall into bed breathless. We play and roll around for hours and give each other pleasure like most happy couples when they have the opportunity.

When we were dating, she used to joke, "Are you going to church to impress me?"

I would give her an honest answer, looking into her eyes, saying, "Shoot! I'm with you because you go to church. I married up, baby." Time spent searching for a good Christian woman to marry had paid off.

It's what I thought I wanted when I swiped right on her Tinder profile. I definitely was searching to improve my life and get closer to God. Hard Christians don't like to hear me say that her purpose in my life was to bring me closer to God. Closer than ever before. This is because of the sacred belief in marriage. I believe everything happens for a reason. Nothing is a coincidence. We operate on God's time and plan.

I shower, throw on my red Nike gym shorts, dark blue shirt, and blue Nikes to match. Leaning in close to kiss her cheek, I whisper in her ear, "Glad I slept in today. I love you Tinderella. I'm gonna' get going. See you later for church."

"Love you Tinderoni. Drive safe. See you later Papi." I tip-toe down the hall and descend the staircase of our year old, model townhome. I saved for three years to purchase the charming two-story unit, falling in love with the lake view.

My father and I installed the custom flooring ourselves. Remnants of a family flooring business sold a few years back. We spent many hours laying cherry red maple in the boys' room. The rest of the home shined in two-toned oak. By the time we were done painting, teal green for the girls' room and baby blue for the boys' room, we were exhausted and proud. It was back breaking work.

I reach the bottom landing and book a hard U-turn, passing the spacious kitchen on the left, the formal dining room, and finally plopping down in my favorite spot on the leather couch. The morning sun glistens, bouncing off the lake through the sliding doors making the chandelier sparkles dance span across the rooms. Powering up my laptop per my morning ritual since 2017, I check my Bitcoin account.

We would have to write another book just on Bitcoin and Blockchain technology. But think about this; everything else has gone digital. Why not money? I'm not saying it will be Bitcoin, especially right now with its volatility. When central banks make their own digital tokens and currency and can control it, in my opinion; it will be adopted. COVID-19 may accelerate this as we transform into a whole new world. Hopefully for the better.

I'm a rookie and have been a rideshare driver for five months part-time. With the expansion of my family upon marriage, and a new home to maintain, we needed the extra money. You can eat off my car and do your hair off the reflection. Clear blue skies betray the heaviness in the air that you can cut with a knife. Departing the family home, my first ride takes me to North Palm Beach. After the drop-off I pull into Tulipan and do a cockpit check, making sure my pens are organized in my cup holder, my gas is half full and no service lights are blinking.

Sauntering up to the counter, the heavy-set waitress is ready to take my order. "Mama dame un Cortadito por favor."

"Grande o chiquito?" asks La Chonga with the big gold hoop earrings.

"Chiquito porfa," I answer and pay. A new fare comes in, "BILILING, BILILING, BILILING." She hands me the coffee. "Gracias mama."

The pick-up is at a dilapidated area off Federal Highway, a run-down no name motel. Brown paint, and what may have passed as white paint many years ago, is chipping off the building. Outside waiting is a middle-aged man with an athletic build. He is dressed sporty in Adidas jogging pants with a white tank top, white sneakers and a white visor to match (cocked to the right). Knowing this area, I take a second to size him up and think, *He is around my build but a little smaller, 5'5 and maybe 140-150 pounds. Nothing I can't handle.*

In front of him sits: one hefty garbage bag full of mystery, one overflowing duffle bag with a broken zipper hanging off the side, and a tiny, closed bag. On his shoulders he wears a food-stained backpack.

Putting the car in park, the overwhelming smell of tobacco greets me and the man yells, "I don't get no respect! Heh, heh, I told my psychiatrist that everyone hates me. He said, don't be ridiculous. Everyone hasn't met you yet." He jumps around, "Ha, ha, my psychiatrist said I was crazy, and I said I wanted a second opinion. He said okay, you're ugly too! Heh, heh, I tell you I get no respect!"

Speaking through my smile, "You're doing Rodney Dangerfield, right?"

He throws his cigarette down, stares at me, squints his serious eyes, and says verbatim, "Motherfucker Mayi! Help me with my shit." He snatches the tiny bag from the gravel. "Now Mayi, I'm gonna' tell you a fucking story. You're gonna' fucking listen. You're not going to fucking interrupt and you're going to listen to everything I fucking say."

Hurriedly grabbing the other two bags, my inner voice cheers me on. *"It's ok, you're built for this. You've been built for this your whole life. Maybe he's mentally ill. The mess from his bag and the sheer number of bags are a giveaway that he may be homeless. Remember, never give anyone the satisfaction of upsetting you over silly things."*

I reply, "Yes, sir," with a wry smirk. His brows scrunch together. His bloated crimson face stares right through me watching me haul the two bags to the trunk. "Man, these are heavy."

He keeps the backpack and the tiny bag with him, opens the front passenger door, and yells, "Yeah, I got my whole life in there. Hey, can I sit up front with you?" Without waiting for permission, he throws the backpack on the floor behind him and keeps the tiny bag up front.

"I prefer if you sat in the back. The rideshare companies prefer that, too. That way you can have your space and I have mine."

"Yeah! Fuck the rideshare companies. I feel better up front."

For the sake of the customer and a smooth ride, I comply by closing the rear door, "Sure why not?" I hop in the front, click my seatbelt, and confirm, "4545 Golf Rd?"

"Yes." We roll and he's telling me the story he so threateningly promised. I have no recollection of what it was about but as we approach the second traffic light, he asks, "And do you know what I did? Do you know what I fucking did, Mayi?"

"You went to-"

He cuts me off and yells, "I told you earlier not to fucking interrupt! Shut the fuck up and just fucking listen! I was being rhetorical, dummy."

I turn with a smile and say soothingly, "Ooo-kayyy," reminding myself to be patient.

We continue our drive, and he's yapping away, "Blah, blah, blah… blah…and then do you know what I did…do you know what I fuckin' did Mayi?" Turning to him and nodding my head up and down without saying a word, listening with a smile. "I blah, blah, blah…," he continues answering his own question.

He goes on with his story. As we approach the next red light just before I-95, a yellow stuffed bird begins pecking at my face. That's right! Rodney Dangerfield is attacking me with a stuffed yellow bird, "Woodstock," Snoopy's friend. You know Snoopy? The white dog from The Peanut comics. Dangerfield, or maybe he is Charlie Brown now, brandishes a calculating smile and pecks at my face with Woodstock repeatedly.

"What the fuck do you think you're doing? I'm sure you don't do that to your friends when they are driving. How the hell do you think that's ok to do to a stranger, especially on a rideshare? What if a cop saw you?"

His face is frozen with the same creepy grin. Still pecking at my cheek, he laughs menacingly, "What! If a cop sees us, he will just think we are gay!"

I swat the stuffed bird away. "No bro! If a cop sees us, he could pull us over for whatever reason he chooses. Then we have to go through a traffic stop for no reason. Not to mention, that is a dangerous distraction. I'm trying to fuckin' drive here man!" Deep breathing settles me down and reminding myself, *"Try to be positive. This ride just started, and it's going to be at least twenty minutes. Keep your cool."*

Once we get on the highway heading south, he apologizes. "I'm sorry, man. I should respect you and your car more. I'm sorry."

"It's alright, man. Go ahead with your story." Immediately as I accept, he pulls a dirty towel from the duffle bag, with yellow and brown gunk all over it.

"Hooock, Pit-tooo, Hooock, Pit-tooo, Hooock, Pit-tooo!" Dangerfield blows his nose as hard as possible three times on the towel and discards it onto my dashboard.

He has pushed me to my limit. "This is a brand new car. Look, bro, I play baseball. In baseball, it's three strikes, and you're out. I've overlooked your outburst and rudeness, but you're on strike two. Get your mucus infected towel off my dash, bro!"

Halfway through the ride and approaching Southern Blvd, he apologizes again. "I'm sorry. Please excuse me. My parents think I'm crazy. I don't know why they think that. They Baker Acted me years ago. They think I'm bipolar. I don't know why they think I'm bipolar. Do you think I'm bipolar Mayi?"

People say the darndest things to me on rides. Before I can even mutter a single word, he reaches into my pen organizer, grabs one of my pens, puts it in between his fingers, and enthusiastically tells me, "You know I can kill you nine different ways with this pen right now?"

In shock, I grab my keys and think, *"Who the fuck says that to a total stranger?"* Managing to place the biggest key between my fingers tightly, I threaten back, "Did you know I can kill you nine different ways with these keys right now?"

His face turns pale, and smiles, "I'm sorry. I wasn't expecting you to say that. I'm sorry. Hey um…I'm not sure the address is right. When we get around there, I'll show you how to get there."

"Ok, man. When we get there, just guide me."

My mind races. *"How do we end this ride without a confrontation because he doesn't even know if the given address is the right address or not."* Leaning heavily towards my window, the only thing I'm worried about is this guy losing the last of his senses and jabbing my neck with a pen.

He turns excitedly, "There is this little homeless lady off of Woolbright as soon as we go east, off the highway on the right. I have some food for her. You think we can stop there so I can drop it off before we go?"

Giving me the opportunity to escape, I happily reply, "Sure! Yeah, bro. No worries. You're talking about where the little blue hut is on Woolbright, right?"

"That's the one." Dangerfield takes off his seatbelt and turns to the backpack on the rear passenger floor. He ruffles through it and finds a to go plate with a plastic see through lid. My nose crinkles up in retreat and I almost vomit. Turning pale, I manage to hold down my morning coffee, roll down the windows and lean even closer to my door. The rotting stench is unforgettable. The food was white and was moving, as if it ran out of the dumpster into his bag. This has become a two-passenger ride. After all this, still not wanting to offend, we ride in silence. To this day, the rancid odor jumps into my nostrils when I see a to-go box.

The exit sign to Woolbright Road is up ahead and we merge onto the exit ramp. Cruising to a stop at the bottom of the Woolbright Road overpass, I'm determined to end this ride no matter what. He has to walk three hundred yards uphill to visit the little old lady. He has one more trick up his sleeve though.

I am parked to the left of the beautiful Boynton Beach Little League baseball field. Dangerfield walks stealthily to the trunk as he says, "Open your trunk. I have one more thing in there for her."

"Sure man. I'll be right here. Trunk is popped."

Watching his every move through the rear-view mirror, Dangerfield pulls out one of the two bags inside the trunk, looks around slyly, quickly opens the bag, and pulls out a handle of Jack Daniels. He swigs up to the sky, "Gulp, Gulp, Gulp."

Shaking my head and mumbling, "This dumb jackass. Fucking people." Dangerfield puts the bottle back. He turns and makes his way to the little blue hut. As he reaches the top, I gather the items he has in my car, open the passenger door and toss them. Running for dear life to the trunk, I grab the remaining bags and place them next to the things tossed out the door. Quicker than a NASCAR pit crew, I hustle back to the drivers' door but, hesitantly stop, turn my head and peek up the overpass to see if he is running back down towards the car. He is sitting down feet crossed Indian style, the sun glistening off his face with a big smile. Cars pass by, but he is enjoying his delicious meal with his friend. I get in my car and burn rubber.

This is one of the only rides I have ever reported. You have to be a real jerk to get reported by me. I'm probably one of the nicest, patient, and considerate drivers you will ever run into. This "Dangerfield," however, is a danger to anyone he rides with and is no laughing matter. Had this been during COVID-19, he would have had to at least wear a mask.

I'm not far from home when I receive a text *"---Papi, you on your way home? Don't forget church starts at 11:30.---"*

Enjoying all the new bells and whistles I howl in the car, "OK, Google. Text wife, I'm not far. Will be home soon."

The technology in these cars is phenomenal. "Texting wife. I'm not far. Will be home soon. Send or change?*"*

"Send."

I rush home to wash the stench of the ride off my body. Running out of the car and up the stairs managing to squeeze in a ten-minute shower and get ready for church, "Babe, I'm dressed. What do you need me to do so we can get moving? It's 10:46."

"Please help the little one with his shoes and do his hair. He wants it up like yours. Make sure he's ready." I hurry into the boy's room.

"Hey, come on. Get off the PS4. I got to do your hair. Where are your shoes? We got to get goin'."

The little one answers, "My shoes are downstairs."

"Come here. Let's do your hair and then get your shoes on. Your momma said you want it spiked up like mine?"

"Yes, Mayi." Little man goes into the Jack and Jill bathroom. I spike up the seven-year-old's hair. He flashes the cutest grin, and we hug.

"Now go put on your shoes and be ready." I turn to mine, "Yo big dog. What about you? You ready to go?"

"Papi, I just gotta' put on my shoes."

"They downstairs, too?"

"Yes."

"Well, let's go. What are you waiting for?" I post up at the door like drill Sgt. McGee. "Come on, let's go. Come on boys, move. Let's move." It's like a New York City subway station up here. Everyone hustles and bustles to get ready.

My wife zig zags from room to room. She hollers, "Papi! Get everyone in the car. We will be right there."

"Ok. Hurry, please! We gotta' go!" We take her car to church since mine is used for ridesharing. The ladies stress us out, always the last to be ready.

The boys rush into the car and turn on the A.C. as habit. The girls run out of the house at the last minute. My wife's forehead is sweating profusely. I smile and hand her a napkin.

"What! What's so funny?"

"Oh, nothing. You look cute when you're mad though."

With a serious tone she swipes at the napkin and replies, "I don't find it funny. You need to help more."

I already know where this is going, and don't feel like fighting. I glance over, "OK. I'm sorry. I'll try and help more." Her silence tells me this answer is not satisfying, but we leave it at that.

We make it to church on time. I had been saved and baptized in the last two months. The church had changed the worship leader at the beginning of April. He is phenomenal. Once there my wife says, "Papi, take the little one to his class. I got these two."

"OK babe. See you same spot as always." Purposely done so I can bond with her little one, and she can bond with mine. I meet my wife in the hall in front of the auditorium. We sit in our normal area in the back row. Two songs in "Oceans (Where Feet May Fail) begins to play. The melody of the singers amazes me, and the lyrics are so powerful.

Louder and louder, the music soars! Then the acoustics drop with the background music and all I hear is the voice of an angel in the choir. Her soft sound penetrates the room with no friction in its path from the stage. For the first time in my life in church, the waterworks begin. I sob like a baby and have no idea why. Looking straight ahead, so no one sees the salt run down my face, quickly wiping it off with my knuckles, but not fast enough, the tears keep coming.

My eyes roll to the right to check on my wife, but she is deep in worship, hands raised to the sky, eyes closed, and singing with her incredible voice. My innocence and youth pour out like water. Guilt and shame from past mistakes float to the surface. My wife grabs a tissue from her purse and hands it to me. She rubs my neck gently, but firmly. I gather myself a few songs later. We pray and sit for the rest of service.

Pastor DS begins, "Change and giving Christian. Forgiving that is. Are you living the life you should be? Are you just walking through life? No acts can get you to heaven. Only through his grace and mercy. Through his forgiveness. Are you as forgiving?"

My eyes warm and fill again. I wonder, *"What the hell is going on with me? Pull yourself together man."* Service comes to an end. We leave on the first song, as usual, pick up the kids and head home. Driving with a blank stare on my face and tuning out the kids in the back seat, my mind ticks at a thousand thoughts per minute. Overwhelm with emotion, I decide to go for a ride in the Slingshot to sort it out.

On a whim, I bought the bat-mobile, despites my wife's misgivings. The black auto cycle has two wheels in the front and one in the back with an open cockpit and two seats.

I park my wife's car on the grass next to the driveway, move my car out of the way, and take the slingshot out of the garage. Roaring the engine and hitting the gas hard, the wind punches me in the face.

My ear-to-ear grin turns upside down when wishing my wife was riding with me but knowing her interests lie elsewhere. She did not like the slingshot. It has been some time since we have laughed on a drive to Nowhere together. For me, these rides put me back to center with nature and God, but lazy drives had not brought us closer as a couple, which was my original hope. After two years of marriage, I was still searching for a deeper connection with my wife. In a sobering haze, my mind wandered back to our earlier conversation.

"I think I'm going for a ride in the slingshot. Want to come?"

"No, Papi. Enjoy your ride. I told the kids I'd take them to the pool."

"I'll meet you guys there, after babe. I'm just gonna' ride for two or three hours."

She grabs my hand, "That will be nice. You know how much they like playing with you in there."

"Yeah, I know."

I am reminded of Dangerfield and his baggage. Baggage we all carry. Some we see; some we don't. If we are blessed, we find someone to share it with, to lighten the load. Turning south on A1A in Lake Worth, I pray. "Lord this is a constant tug of war back and forth. I believe in you. Don't give up on me. I won't give up on you. Help me. Help me Lord with these inner demons and worries. Help me forgive. Help me keep my family close and practice patience. Help me be merciful and graceful. In the name of Jesus, I beg you, Amen!"

LIFE AND RIDES BEFORE CHRIST

PART I : Tri-County Lines

SAT/ 3:30 A.M., "ERR...ERR...ERR," the alarm clock screams, pressuring me to get up for the scheduled ride. If I can make this ride, my day changes astronomically. If I don't, my day will drag on like a Florida hurricane watch. This ride is an easy $35-$50 toward my goal of $200 per day. 5 A.M.-10 A.M., 1 P.M.-6 P.M. and 9 P.M.-2 A.M. are what I call the "Power Hours." To the airport; from the airport. To work, from work. 7 A.M. comes around, and its trips to drop kids at elementary and high school. 9:30 A.M., and it's middle school drop-off. Driving in the mornings, means no driving nights.

"Mwah," my lips barely brush my wife's forehead, so as not to wake her. Throwing on my red polo shirt, jeans, and two-toned running shoes, I hustle out the door like many mornings before.

The skunk odor of the burning blunt calms me. Leaning against my car hood and exhaling, the smoke wafts across the glistening white moon. Knowing the sun will rise soon, my left foot stomps out the roach, and I slide my body into the driver's seat to turn on the tunes and hear "Best on Earth," by Russ. I grew up on hard hip hop, R&B, reggaeton and Latin vibes. My first call chimes.

Putting the car into gear and heading northwest from Lake Worth, I arrive timely as usual, jump out of my car, open the backdoor, and confirm, "Picking up for Gary?"

In unison two voices reply, "That's us."

"THUMP, THUMP," I close the doors once they are safely seated.

Gary continues, "That was awfully nice of you. You're the first driver to open and close the doors for us ever. This is my wife, Sam."

"Hi, Sam."

"Hi."

"Gary, Sam…3455 Powerline Road, Pompano?"

In tandem with a slur, "Yes sir." They pull down the center armrest, insert their red cups into the cup holders, and share a magazine.

I look in the rear view. "Well, the way I see it, you don't open your own doors when you pay for a limo. I know this isn't limo service, but you shouldn't have to open your doors when you pay for a ride. It's a little service I like to provide, and we all win. I get to step out of the car and stretch my legs at the same time."

"Well, we really appreciate that young man."

"My pleasure. Hey guys, if it's hot or windy back there and you want the windows up, just let me know." The windows are purposely left down to conserve gas on A.C. and as part of my routine to feel you out.

"Thank you, sir. We are cool right now."

"Cool. I'll roll them up before we get on the Turnpike, so we don't have to listen to the loud wind."

"Thank you," they say, focused on the magazine, turning it page by page.

I quickly glance at the app and see I have half a mile until reaching the Ronald Reagan Turnpike. I close all the windows and turn on the A.C. Merging onto the Turnpike from Lake Worth Road. I wave my hand in front of the A.C. and ask, "Temperature O.K?"

"Yes, sir. Great, thank you."

"You comfortable with seventy-five on the highway?"

"No one has ever asked that before. Thank you. You can do eighty-five if you want." They take a sip out of their red solo cups and continue perusing their magazine.

"I ask because I picked this guy up, and from the moment I picked him up, he was complaining that he was late for work. He gets in my car and says, I'm late for work! I'm late for work! Can you step on it? I said, Yeah, I can step on it, but if you're late for work, why would you pick a shared ride? If it picks up another rider, I have to go get them, and you're going to be even later. He sucks in his lips, and I can tell he's a little upset and said, I don't know, man. It was cheaper."

I turn down the volume then peek in the mirror. She's going through the magazine intently. Gary has his left hand on her right leg caressing her, ears peeled. I look straight ahead and continue. "Forty seconds later, a ride comes in, and I tell him, hey man, I'm sorry. A ride came in and I'm required to get them. He was pissed and said, you gotta' do what you gotta' do. To make a long story short, I do seventy-two in a sixty-five to help him out on the highway. Speeding is a safety issue. They will block you from the apps for it, but I got ahead of it. Immediately after the ride, I wrote in about him complaining about the ride from the moment he got in the car. Whining that he was late and being frustrated about having to pick someone up. I let the rideshare company know he is looking for a free ride and that I educated him on the types of rides. Sure enough, I receive a text from them after the ride that they had a complaint from a customer about speeding and if I cared to share any feedback on the ride. So I wrote back, due to your lack of transparency and anonymity, I have no idea what ride you're talking about because I conduct every single ride the same, but if I had to guess, I would guess it's the ride that I already wrote you about. Take a look at that email and go one further. It was a shared ride. Call the other passenger and see how he felt about the ride. Thank you."

"You were only doing seven over. I'll go crazy if you don't do at least seventy-five."

"Well, Gary, it was a good lesson learned. I try to take something from every ride if I can. I came up with a plan to avoid this in the future. Different people have different comfort levels of speed they prefer when strangers are driving them. So now, I just communicate and ask if you're comfortable with seventy-five. I have had a few older people tell me they prefer me to do the sixty-five-speed limit. I just stay in the right lane and cruise."

"Well, Mayi, that's greatly appreciated. Thank you."

"Yeah, man. No worries. Here, enjoy the tunes."

Gary looks down at the magazine. "Wave" by Meghan Traynor plays. I zone out driving and seventeen minutes later pass the green Glades Rd. exit sign for Boca Raton. It's 4:54 A.M. The lyrics to Drake, "Best I Ever Had," are banging out of the speakers. In the background I hear very faintly, "Oh shoot," from the woman as she moves around and barely hovers over the seat. Sometimes I just don't understand adults. Instead of just telling me, she whispers to Gary, "Shh. I just spilled the drink. What do I do?"

Gary whispers back, "I don't know. I don't have anything."

She mumbles, "I'm going to sit here and let my shorts clean and absorb it somehow," and continues looking through the magazine.

Another Drake song plays, "Hotline Bling."

Struggling to hear Gary and his wife, they speak just loud enough for me to decipher snippets. "...no not this one honey...what about this black one? Oh no, that one is too big...what about this one?...that one's not too bad...oh, these are nice..." They simultaneously turn the page. Still heading south, we eventually come to a halt at the arrival address. My eyes fall upon the neon sign, "Mega Emporium Sex Shop," in Pompano Beach. I pop the car in park, hop out, and open the doors.

With a crimson face, Gary jumps out, and hands me a $10 bill. "Thanks, man. It was a great ride."

"My pleasure Gary. Glad it was smooth for you. You kids have fun in there."

Sam's face is cherry red, matching her husband's, and they both reply, "Thanks!"

After they are out of sight and inside the emporium safely, I reach in and grab the green towel kept in the front passenger seat for spills. While wiping the light grey leather seat down of something sticky I think, *"All they had to do was say something. You want to be slick? I'll be slick."* I remove the Emporium's dildo catalogue she left open on the seat. She used the page selling penis lollipops to hide the smear of alcohol. Something about this makes me laugh, *"Well this was a nice $35 ride to start the day."*

Walking back from throwing away the catalogue at the green dumpster nearby, "BILILING, BILILING, BILILING (45+mins)," a new ride request flashes on my phone. The "Money Maker" just came in. One or two "Money Makers" will make your day. "Money Makers" are rides that pay $40 or more. From my current location, I'm going to end up either deep south into Miami, or back up north to Palm Beach.

I arrive at "Hot Shots," a popular sports bar and wait in my car at the pick-up spot. Looking down at my watch, it's almost 5:30 A.M. Two gorgeous blondes exit the bar and are standing outside alone. They have light eyes and are wearing sexy white lacy tops. One is wearing a jean skirt and the other white shorts, both with 6' inch white peep toe heels. In a flash, I make my way around to the passenger rear door, "Pick up for Vanessa?"

They stumble back and with eyes as big as owls, "You're Mayi?"

"Yes, ma'am."

"Whoa! You scared us. We thought you were going to mug us the way you jumped out of your car so quickly. We have never seen a driver get out of his car before."

"I'm sure that's because you have never had a driver open and close the door for you either." They both duck in through the same passenger side, and I close the door behind them. "THUMP!"

"Vanessa, I'd like to confirm. 1111 Toni Pena Road, Jupiter?"

"Yes!"

"Ladies, if it gets hot or windy back there and you want the windows up just let me know. This is your ride, and I want it to be as comfortable for you as possible."

"Thanks, Mayi. Yeah, go ahead and roll up the windows."

"Yes, ma'am. Will do. Are you ladies comfortable with seventy-five on the highway?"

"You can do one-hundred if you want. Just get us home safe. We are exhausted." I roll up the windows and turn on the A.C. Throwing on "Climax" by Usher we head toward I-95.

Vanessa's friend asks, "What are you doing up so late? You been driving all night?"

"Nah. Just got up. I've been at it since 3:30 A.M. You know, the early bird catches the worm in this business. You guys are my second job and I'm almost done with my morning. Besides, it's Saturday. On Saturday, I work a few hours in the morning for some extra change." I glance at the time on my dash. "The question is what are you guys doing way down here from Jupiter at 5:37 A.M?"

"We needed a change of scenery, so we came to party in Ft. Lauderdale last night. Ended up here. So, what's your story? You from New York? You sound like you're from New York. You got that New York vibe."

"That's so funny, get that a lot. Still trying to figure that one out. I guess when I say some words, the way I say them sounds like I'm from New York. I have a lot of friends from New York and have been there many times. Is that a good thing or a bad thing? Because when I was there, they always seemed so pissed off."

"Oh no, definitely a good thing. You jumped out of the car so fast. Jumped in. New York guys are always on the go. Your choice in music. You give off a cool vibe. How old are you?"

"Thanks. I'll take that compliment. I'm forty-one. Born in Cuba. Been here since I was three. Grew up in wonderful Boca Raton. I love that city. Got married and we live in west Lake Worth. How old are you guys? Oh, is the temp, ok?"

I glance in the mirror and they flip their hair in tandem. Vanessa chimes in, "Yeah, the temperature is fine. Wait, you're forty-one?"

"Yes, ma'am"

"Wow, you look great for forty-one." Vanessa's friend continues, "I'm Sarah. I'm twenty-nine, and Vanessa is twenty-seven. We thought you were thirty-two, maybe thirty-four."

"Thanks again. I'm flattered. You're both very pretty. Always remember your body is like a car. If you change the oil and do the maintenance, it will last you a long time. If you drink plenty of water, get your rest in, eat the right foods, and exercise, you and your body will look younger and feel better, too. I'm always in the gym. Keeps me young."

"It most certainly does."

I feel my cheeks warming and smile like a kid on a playground, "Thanks." There are a lot of red-faced moments in a car when you're driving strangers around. People are bolder when it's a short interaction.

I turn the music up one notch. Not loud enough so that we can't hear each other, just a tad. "Great song," I say. "Como Yo Le Doy" by Pitbull is pumping. They sit back and play on their phones. We cruise I-95, drawing near Indiantown Road. The night is dark as sin, but you can feel the sun is about to break through.

Sarah whispers to Vanessa, "I can't wait to get home and hit the bong. We still have some pot left, right?"

"Yeah, we do…Oh, wait, no, we did the last of it before we left."

"Can we call someone? Who can we call?"

"Sarah, who are we going to call that is up at 6 A.M. in the morning for pot?"

Sarah sighs, leans forward, and gently rubs my right elbow.

I think, *"Is this really happening? I must be imagining things."* She continues to rub on my elbow with her right hand and asks, "Do you have any pot?"

Turning briefly over my right shoulder, "Wha…What did you say?"

Sarah repeats, louder. "Do you have any pot?"

"Oh, you mean do I have any weed?"

"Yes. Do you have any weed, pot?"

"You girls cops? Undercover?"

"Are you serious, dude? Do you really think we are undercover? Come on!"

"No, I didn't." Smirking, "Did I hear you right? Did I hear you guys talking about a bong back there?"

Sarah is still rubbing on my elbow. Vanessa answers proudly, "Yeah. We have a nice two-footer. If you have some pot, you can come in and smoke with us."

"Are you girls trying to make me the next rideshare story? I don't know. I don't want to be on the news."

Sarah moves her free hand to cup my ear and whispers, "We are harmless. We just want to smoke. You have nothing to worry about, my dear."

Now, you must be wondering why I had not removed her hand from my elbow yet. To this day, I'm not sure why I didn't. At that moment my mind raced, *"She is just flirting to get what she wants. This is no big deal. Man, I would really like to hit that two-footer. It's been a while."*

Here I encounter my two deadliest sins. The ones I pray about daily. A double whammy. My insatiable appetitive for weed and women. Luckily my wife suppressed my need for any other woman. I lusted for her.

I have a moment of weakness. "Well, ladies, today is your lucky day. I have some Krypto in the trunk. It was for when I end my shift, but I guess I can share and make you guys my last ride of the day."

"Wait you're serious? You have pot in the trunk, and you have been listening to us this whole time, giving us a hard time?" Sarah says while smacking my shoulder.

"Well...I don't know you. I had to feel you out. You think I'm just going to tell a stranger right off the bat that I have what you're looking for? Gotta' be smarter than that."

We park in front of a tall white and beige building. A brown four-foot railing encompasses the intercoastal waterway. Manicured shrubs two-feet high hug the railing. "Nice place you guys got here."

"Thanks. We met as nurses and have been best friends ever since. We bought it together three years ago." I jump out, open, and close the doors for them. "THUMP, THUMP!"

They make their way to their front door while I go to the trunk to retrieve the pot. I drop the small plastic baggie of green in my pocket. Sarah stops me at the doorway. "Wait. I gotta' make sure you're not carrying any weapons."

"Are you serious?" I ask as she starts to pat me down. She pats my shoulders, runs her hands down my back, squeezes my butt, and grabs my penis. I grimace my face slightly, move back from her grasp and make eye contact.

With a huge smile across her face, "You see, I knew you were carrying a weapon."

"Whoa! Ah, I see what you're doing. Pretty slick. I might have used that line a few times myself." I brush past her because all I can think about is hitting that bong. Once inside the house, we sit on the couch in the living room. Sarah grabs the two-foot bong on the glass table. "Let me see that thing. Let me fill it," I say and she scooches closer to me to light the bong.

Sarah hands me the bong next and wafting out smoke from her lungs, whispers, "That's not all you're filling this morning."

Staring at the bong, I chuckle. "Oh. Is that so?" I know better than to look her in the eye this time. She may take it as an invitation.

Out of the corner of my eye, I can see Sarah bite her lip, "Uh, huh."

I pack the bong and hand it to Vanessa. "Be careful. This is some really good stuff. It's from Boca. My boys in Boca have money. They only buy the best."

Vanessa takes a short hit. "Bloop, bloop, bloop." She doesn't clear it and hacks out a lung. Sarah and I laugh hysterically as Vanessa coughs, covers the bong top with her palm, and through bloodshot eyes manages to pass it to Sarah. Sarah attempts to clear out what Vanessa left behind. "Bloop, bloop, bloop." She coughs out a lung as well.

We all laugh like hyenas, and it's my turn. I finish the little bit they left. It had been years since I'd hit a bong. I grab my baggie and pack myself a generous helping. My wife did not smoke. That's really what brought me to this time and place. What had not mattered in our early dating days, had become a rift between us.

"Bloop, bloop, bloop, bloop, bloop, bloop." I clear the whole hit, hold my THC-filled breath tight, and listen to both girls squeal in awe.

"Daaaaamn."

I let out the hit. "I got lungs of steel ladies. I've been smoking for a long time. Remember, you two are babies. I'm an old man."

Vanessa utters, "You're not that old, and you're pretty cool." We all lay back on her black leather couch.

"Thank you." I respond.

We are high as kites. Thirty minutes feels like hours. We are chilling, and I'm minding my own business, in my own world, with my squinty, but alert eyes. I catch Sarah shift even closer to me. In a normal state of mind, I probably wouldn't think anything of it. When I smoke, my conscience rises up. That voice is the one I have never been able to ignore. *"I don't want to be the next story. What am I doing here? This is totally inappropriate. My wife would not be happy. I would not be happy if the tables were turned. I don't want to be on the news. Something consensual can happen here, and it can still be turned into something it wasn't. I'm married. What am I doing here?"*

I abruptly stand up. "Ladies, thank you so much for letting me smoke with you. I haven't hit a bong in years. It was awesome meeting you both. You are both very attractive and friendly. Here. This is for you guys. Enjoy and don't smoke it all in one place. I gotta' get back to work."

They stand up and give me a quick hug and kiss on the cheek goodbye. "You sure you have to leave?"

Flashing through all the potential chaos that could occur, my skin gets hot, my cheeks burn red, "As much as I would love to stay, I have to get back home to my wife."

Walking me to the door Sarah sighs and says, "Whoever your wife is, she is a very lucky woman. She should be proud and happy to have such a fine, handsome, loyal man. Not once did you try to hit on either of us."

"Believe me, it wasn't easy. Any man would be lucky to have either of you. Anyone would have taken you this morning. Twenty years ago, I wouldn't have cared or hesitated, but I'm trying to live right. I have a beautiful wife at home that I love."

"Awww," Sarah whispers while handing me a $20 dollar bill.

"What's this? What's this for?"

"That's for you. For such an awesome ride and for being such a gentleman."

I lean in and give her another kiss on the cheek. "Thank you again. You guys didn't have to."

"We know. You didn't have to be so nice either."

"You two have a Merry Christmas."

"Hope Santa is good to you, Mayi."

Rushing to my car, I stumble, but catch my balance. I sit down and look desperately for my sunglasses. It's blinding outside. I look at my phone again. This ride just paid $48. I have completed two rides and I'm sitting on $113. Turning on my car and staring at the roof for a moment, I begin to laugh. I pull out and head towards the ocean.

One of the perks of the job is that sooner or later, you're going to be close to the water. That's where I take 85% of my breaks. The clock on the dash reads 7:36 A.M. I turn down the music to enjoy the elements. It's a short five-minute ride tops. The palm trees stand still this brisk morning. The sky is a living canvas with strokes of reds, pinks, purples, and oranges. My wife never partook in sunrises though I asked her to accompany me many times. She was not a morning person while I embrace the sun's rays.

After parking, I walk the sidewalk and sit on a lonely bench that faces the beach. The air remains cool while my fingers roll up another blunt, watching the sun remove the shadows around me. My getaways consist of the beach, slingshot drives, and visiting a baseball field.

Strangely, the change in temperature from warm to cold always causes me to smoke more. I finish and throw the roach down feeling an urge for a Cuban "cortadito." I wander back to my car, jump in, plug in the phone, and speed away from the ocean. I arrive at "Havana," my favorite Cuban restaurant in all of Palm Beach County. This is my "Cheers." Strolling to the corner window, the servers greet me. "Hola Mayi! Como estas? Como te va manejando hoy?"

"Muy bien ninas. Ya tu sabes. La misma mierda, otro día. Margerita… mama dame un-"

"Ya papi. Aqui te tengo el cortadito."

"Wow! Usted si me quieren. I love you guys. Por eso yo vengo aqui."

"Y nosotros a ti papito,"Margerita says in her cute green and red elf outfit. She blows air from her lips upwards to move the ball from the tip of the red cone hat out of her way and onto the other side of her face.

"Sabes, dame una croqueta y pastelito para la esposita."

"Toma, Dale!"

"Gracia amores. Que se quiden y las veo pronto. Las quiero mucho."

"Dale papo. Quidete. Te veo pronto."

I am a regular at Havana and know all the servers in the outer cafe, especially Margerita. They know my order before I say the words from visiting almost every other day. I pay my check and keep it moving towards home sweet home.

I manage to drag myself in the door and make it to my spot on the couch. To my surprise the kids are still sleeping. Turning on ESPN to the realization its only 9:56 A.M. reminds me of the long day that lays ahead. Princess is sleeping upstairs.

In what feels like a heartbeat later, there is a tapping sensation on my shoulder. "Papi wake up. Wake up. I want some salsa."

Rolling over, my eyes open to see my wife hovering over me. "What time is it? Is it late?"

"It's the afternoon. Come on. Get up. I want some salsa."

"You really just woke me up right now for salsa?" I roll back over and mumble, "Babe, wake me up in like one or two hours. Then, I'll make the salsa."

"No Papi. Come on. I want some salsa now!"

"Babe, if you want some salsa now, everything you need is in the kitchen. You know how to make it. Everything is there. If you will let me rest, I'll make it when I get up."

She wiggles her way grumbling to the kitchen, and yells, "God, you're so lazy! You don't do anything around here! You don't help out! You're so selfish and lazy!"

I sit up on the couch and twist in her direction. "I'm so tired of hearing you say that! I work my ass off just to pay this mortgage! A mortgage I told you I couldn't afford comfortably. You said you'd help. You haven't. You offered to get more hours or find a little part-time job. You haven't. You enjoy having your Tuesdays, Thursdays, and weekends off, right? Well, one of us has to work a fulltime job. I haven't complained about busting my ass, but I'm tired of you going off on me when I don't jump as high as you want me to, when you want me to." I slam back down on the couch.

She continues yelling from the kitchen, "Oh, don't turn this around on me. You always do that. I do so much around this house. You never help."

My voice raises louder to drown her out. "The difference is that I know and recognize the things you do around the house. Do you realize you start like 95% of our fights over nothing? We are arguing over salsa because you're so damn selfish. Instead of making it yourself, you wake me up to make it. You know I've been up working so all of you can sleep peacefully."

She screams, "Well, it's your fault we are arguing because you should know how to handle me better! You know how I am. How my anxiety gets to me!"

"Are you listening to yourself? How can you pick fights with me and then blame me because I don't react better? Did you not see how calm I was when you woke me out of a deep sleep? You continued to push. You pick, and pick, and pick. Do you even care that the kids are upstairs? You don't get to start fights with me, then blame me because I don't react better because you have anxiety. That's total bullshit."

She grabs her keys, standing at the door with her hand on her hip and her purse on her shoulder. "You're such an asshole. I'm going to the gym and then grocery shopping."

"I was going to ask you, but since this afternoon has gone so well, I'm going to tell you. Instead of waking up early tomorrow to drive, I'm just going to go tonight, so I can wake up for church tomorrow."

"That's fine. You know I prefer you not working Sunday mornings anyways."

"Yes, I know. But you know how much I hate driving at night. Especially on Saturday night. All the crazies, but you wouldn't care. Tomorrow when we are a bit calmer, we can talk about Christmas."

"OK. Bye!"

"Bye, Felicia!"

My wife stomps out of the house as fast as her legs will allow her. As for me, I need to rest. It's going to be a long night. I grab my phone, setting an alert for 7 P.M.

"ERR…ERR…ERR!" My alarm sounds off on my phone, and I pop up feeling like a million bucks. I run upstairs, take a quick shower and get ready to go. It's a quarter till 8 P.M. My wife isn't home yet. My frustrations keep me from calling her. I figure she will be home soon and is out blowing off some steam. I hop in the car and start my route towards Havana with my apps on, stopping at the Cumberland Farms on the corner of Jog Road and Hypoluxo Road to fill up. Then, continuing north on Jog Road, stopping at the PNC bank to pull out some cash. PNC ATM's hand out $1's, $5's, and $10's. I strategically pull out $19 to have some change handy.

"BILILING, BILILING, BILILING!" The first job of the night chimes in forcing me to forgo my "cortadito." I arrive at the corner pick up and pull in. It's a new thing the rideshare companies are trying. Corner pickups. Dumbest thing ever. It's tougher to open the door because the customer is usually outside and ready to jump in your car. I pull into the parking lot and the customer opens the front passenger door to sit down. I hate this, but let it slide for the sake of a smooth ride.

I confirm, "Martin? Headed to the Mad Hatter?"

"Oh yes, darling. I love my British pubs. They remind me of home. I'm going to a Christmas party. You want to come to the party and be my date? You know darling, I was right there at the corner waiting."

"I know, Martin. I saw you, but there's no way I was gonna stop at that corner. Martin, it makes no sense. All I think about is picking someone up at the corner and the guy behind me, not paying attention, rear-ending me. Too risky. It's safer to pick you up in the parking lot." Waving at the navigation screen, continuing, "You should see some of the dangerous corners this thing tries to get me to stop at. No way."

"So, are you coming to the party as my date or what?"

"Martin, I'm flattered. Hate to tell you, but I'm straight and married. I love the purple Mad Hatter hat you got on and the earrings are a nice touch."

"Thank you, darling. Is the dark red lipstick too much? I thought it would make the pink strappy top and shorts pop."

"I'm not a fan of dark red lipstick, but the tight white shorts definitely pop!"

Martin rummages through his purse and says, "You're a good-looking bloke. Nice and young. I'm sure your wife is hot, but I promise she doesn't give a blow job like me. Why don't we start you off with that? Let me give you a blow job."

Not believing my ears, I do a double take. "What did you just say? Did I hear you right?"

"Yes, you did, darling." He bats his eyelashes at me, crosses his feet, puts both hands on his leg, one hand on top of another like the Queen of England would sit, and says, "Just let me suck your cock. I'm sixty-three. Most guys I mess around with are married to women. I suck a mean cock."

My face reddens like a tomato. "Martin, you're not the first guy, and you're definitely not going to be the last guy, to offer me that. I'm flattered, but it's not going to happen bro. You can suck the best cock in the world, but mine would not even get hard. I'm not attracted to men. I'm sorry."

He turns away, "Don't knock it till you try it! Well, let me try the bell-end. If I can get you hard, you let me finish."

"Negative, Ghost Rider. I'm sure I don't have to try anything with you. My wife is smoking and I'm into chicks. Now, Martin, I'm being nice to you because I have gay cousins in my family and the choices you make in life are yours to live with. Don't push it. It's not happening."

Approaching The Mad Hatter, Martin turns to me, "I'm sorry about that. It's just you're such a good-looking bloke."

"Martin, it's cool, man. Believe it or not, growing up in South Florida, I'm used to it. Guys hit on me all the time. I don't know why, but they do. I gave a gay kid a chance at true friendship with me once. We were friends for eight years until he crossed the line, not once, but twice. Funny enough, my cousin, Yez, would tell you that I could pick up the hottest woman and the hottest man in the room. It's just not for me. Please respect that the same way I am respecting you. Anyways Martin, enjoy your Christmas party."

"Thank you, darling. Maybe if I'm lucky, you will still be driving tonight, and I'll get you for the ride home. Let's see what you say then."

Pointing at Martin and laughing back thinking, *"This guy won't give up."*

"Yeah, if you're lucky. I don't usually drive late or at night."

Martin exits my car, closes the door, blows me a kiss and walks into the bar. What a way to start my night. It's 8:53 P.M. pre-COV-ID-19 in South Florida, and anything can happen, but I have never been matched with the same rider twice in one night.

After quite a few rides I end up in the wealthy playground of Singer Island. A call comes in for a round trip at 11:20 P.M. I do my normal spiel opening and closing the door, "THUMP," and confirm, "Don?"

"Yes, sir, that's me."

"Don, we are doing a round trip to Riviera and back here?"

"Yes, sir, we are."

"Don, if it's hot or windy and you want the windows up, just let me know?"

"OK, I will, but this is perfect."

"Cool!"

Don makes me wonder. *"Why is a rich old man ordering a round trip into Riviera and back?"* We are about halfway on the first leg of the trip when Don leans forward and says, "Hey do you think you could...could stop at the gas station so I can get some cigarettes?"

"Yeah, man. No worries. This is your ride. We can go wherever you want."

He mumbles, "Thank you."

Three minutes pass by, and Don rises again. "Hey, man do you... you think... you could...stop at the gas station so I can get some cigarettes?"

"Don, I already told you yes, man. I'm looking to stop at a gas station on the route." Don leans back, and I worry to myself, "*What the hell is going on with him? Those pauses were for ten, fifteen seconds. At least he picked up where he left off every time. He's fucked up on something. Just keep him calm.*"

We pull up to the closest gas station. Don gathers himself together and grabs a wad a cash out of his pocket. Opening the door, and holding it wide, he barks, "Hey man, you need anything?"

"No, Don. I appreciate it, but I'm good. Thank you, sir."

Don emerges coveting a soda and candy tightly in his hands. I'm still trying to figure him out. Something just isn't right. Back on the road, Don rises up again. "Hey, when we get..." I look back to discover what these long pauses are all about and see Don's eyes rolling back in his head, his mouth gaping and tongue wildly curled back under his front bottom teeth. I have to look forward to drive, and he continues after that pause, "...there can you wait and please not leave me here?"

"Don, you have a round trip. Why would I leave you here?"

"We are not going into a very good neighborhood."

"Don't worry, Don. I got you."

We drive up to Gatlin Lane in Riviera Beach. This is "The Hood" of hoods, and it's almost midnight. I turn the corner slowly. There are six black dudes hanging out on the block, illuminated under one working streetlamp. I immediately backtrack and regret my words.

"Mayi park over here. I'll be right back." Don points to a dark corner about twenty feet from the group.

"Don, if someone approaches my car, I'm gone. If they get in front of it, I'm running them over. Just making that clear." I turn off my headlights.

"I understand." Don gets out of my car and walks over to the men. My head is on a swivel and the adrenaline causes my palms to start sweating. Looking in all my mirrors, scanning the street, checking behind my car and to the sides, I finally witness the hand exchange.

Don returns to my car right after. I turn on my headlights and peel out. You can hear crickets in my car for those first few minutes. Then, Don leans forward again. "Hey, man. Thank you for that. I know it wasn't ideal."

"Don, what are you on? What is your drug of choice and what did we just get? Don't lie to me because I'm not stupid."

"I'm on heroin. That's what I like, but we just got some Oxy's. My heroin guy isn't around. Mayi, I didn't want to tell you. Please don't report me to the rideshare company. That's what another driver did with the other app company. I can't use them anymore. Please! I'll give you a good tip."

"Don, my man, I'm not going to report you. I am going to protect myself first and take off the moment something crazy or fishy happens. Look, the way I see it is like this, and this is where I disagree with the rideshare companies. They want us to report you if you get in our cars hammered or high. I'm not going to do that. I think that defeats the purpose. I have two rules. You respect my car and the other rider if you did a shared ride. If you do that, I don't care how intoxicated you are. If you get reported enough or declined enough, you might get behind that wheel. Don, I don't know about you, but the way I saw you on the way there, I would rather have you high in my car than driving high in the car that can potentially T-bone me. Now, I don't intentionally do drug runs, but typically by the time I know, it's too late. Besides, I know you're going to get home safe with me at the wheel."

"You're a really good person, man. You're a cool driver."

If compliments were gold bars, I would be as rich as Don. I glance in the rearview mirror, "Yeah, tell my wife that." Don is nodding in and out again from his heroin high while we make our way back to his cozy condo. The night is clear. Stars light up the sky. I roll up to the entrance, "Don...Don, wake up. Wake up, buddy." I jump out and open his door. I nudge him a few times until he comes to.

"Oh, man. Thank you." He gets out and hands me a $20 bill. "For all your trouble."

"Thank you, sir. I appreciate that."

A call comes into my queue. I won't know the destination until after I accept the pickup, but I hope it takes me off the Island and not into Riviera. Riviera has been the scene of numerous rideshare car jackings. I reach the rideshare pickup at a cute little blue and yellow villa with white roman columns. I get out of my car, look at my phone and see three minutes left on the countdown. When the rider comes out, I open the door and confirm, "Mark?"

"Yes, sir. Thank you. She's with me, too." Mark flops into the car. I close the door. "THUMP!"

"Wait one sec, hun. I'll get that door for you." I run around the back of my car and open the drivers' rear door. She falls in, and I close her door, "THUMP!" I open and close my door, "THUMP!" I confirm the address, letting out a sigh of relief. "Aaah, Hyatt, Downtown West Palm Beach?"

Mark replies, "Yes, sir."

Mark is a little overweight and is wearing monochrome grey from head-to toe, even his skin looks a little grey for a white dude. His hair is styled like a playboy, but looks greasy, and he smells of sickly-sweet sweat. He is with a skinny black woman wearing jeans and a teal shirt that has seen better days as well.

Mark asks, "Listen, there is one stop we have to make first. Is that O.K? I'll take care of you. I'll give you an extra $20 bill. I'll take care of you. You're in good hands."

"No worries. You don't have to do that. What's the address of the extra stop?"

We are crossing the Singer Island bridge, and I spot Peanut Island to the left. The sky is clear, and the stars are still shining bright on this godforsaken dirty night out.

Mark turns to the girl, "Babe, you got that address? Give him the address."

She responds to him, "Wait, beetch, I'm looking for it. Give me a minute."

"Well, what the fuck? Don't keep the man waiting. You just had it."

"Shit, calm down. There I found it. 1801 Greenwood Ave., Riviera."

I hit a couple of buttons on my monitor. "Watch this, guys. Car's pretty cool. O.K. Google. Map 1801 Greenwood Ave. Riviera."

"*Mapping 1801 Greenwood Ave, Riviera Beach.*"

Mark asks, "That's not that far, right?"

"Not from here. Not the best area, but not far."

"I got you, buddy. Here let me give you this now." Mark drops a $20 bill on my center console.

"Thank you, man. You didn't have to do that."

"I'm from Boston. We don't fack around in Boston, you know what I mean."

"I hear ya. What brings you down here?"

"Work. I'm in commercial collections. I'm always traveling."

I stop the car. "Guys, we are here."

"Mayi, she's going to get out and get something and come right back. Three to five minutes. I'm going to stay in the caar with you."

"No worries. O.K."

Mark's companion wanders out of the car, disappearing out of view for two minutes, then stumbles back to my car window. "This ain't the right address. You sure you brought us to the right address?"

"Yes. I brought you to 1801 Greenwood Ave. like you said."

"I didn't say Greenwood Ave. I said Georgia Ave."

"No. You said-"

Mark interrupts, "Come on. Get the fack back in the caar. Shut up. Get in the caar."

She gets in the car and points at me accusingly. "He brought us to the wrong address."

"No, I did-"

Mark interrupts again. "Na, he didn't. He brought us to the address you said. You said Greenwood Ave. So, it's not here? You're saying it's Georgia Ave?"

"Yes, beetch. Damn, that's what I said."

"Yo Mayi! How far is that from here and where we are going? I got you, man. I'll throw you another $20 bill." I turn the car on and head towards Georgia Ave.

"You don't have to do that, man, but Georgia Avenue is around where you're going to be heading. It's also not the best area. It's about ten minutes from the Hyatt."

"That's cool. You think we can make that stop?"

"Yeah, Mark. No worries." I hop on I-95 South. "Temperature O.K.? You comfortable with seventy-five on the highway?"

"Everything is great!" Mark replies. I turn the music up as much as I can without seeming rude. I am forced to hear some of the conversations in the backseat because Mark is extremely loud and doesn't care. "You know this better be good. This better work out here because if not we are done looking."

"Yes, bae. I got you, bae. You know that." She promises.

"No. I don't know that. You ripped me off twice already."

"Bae, I had nothing to do with that. You know that. I would never do that to you baby. You are so sweet." Her attempts at flattery fail.

"What the fack you mean? You had everything to do with it. You made the faking deal. Don't fack me on this."

"Bae, I got you."

They continue bickering in the back seat until turning onto Georgia Avenue. I come to a stop at 1801 Georgia Ave. "O.K. here."

"Go! Hurry back." Mark commands. She opens the door, stumbles around, and dips behind one of the houses. "Hey, man. I'm sorry about all this. You obviously know what's going on. She's getting me some coke. I know you know she's a prostitute. Just out trying to have some fun, you know. Take her back and faack a little."

"Yeah, Mark. I know what's going on. You're on drugs, we are running around to get you more drugs and you're trying to get laid. It's none of my business. Please do all of us a favor. We are in a bad area. Help me keep a lookout. You look right by you, and I'll look left. You never know with these people. Your lady looks a little screwed up and I'm not dying tonight."

"Don't worry. We ain't dying tonight. I'm strapped. You see anything, you take off. I don't need this shit that bad. I don't think she's faacked up. She told me she doesn't do any drugs. I think she's a good girl. I believe her."

"Mark, I'm not saying you're naive, but that girl is definitely on something. Can't you tell by the way she's been talking or stumbling? She is on something, and I think it could be heroin."

"I don't know. Well, she hasn't done anything in front of me, but she has gone to the bathroom a bit. You sure?"

As she walks back, she stumbles around and almost falls in front of my headlights. Gravel bits spray into the air, hitting the front hood of my car. She manages to stretch out her arms and catches herself using the hood for support. I look back at Mark, my lips stretching across my face in a thin line, my eyes open wide with a disapproving nod. She ducks back in my car and says, "Go. Let's go." I take off to the Hyatt.

Mark begins to bicker with the Lady of the Night again. "I thought you said you weren't faacked up. Why did you lie to me? You didn't have to give me this whole story. That's faacked up."

"Mark, I'm a fucking escort. What do you expect from me? You know what? When we get back, just call me another rideshare. I thought you were sweet, but you ain't. It's time for me to go."

He backtracks. "No. It's no big deal. You're coming back up with me. I got us more drugs. You're coming up. It will be fun. You cost me a little more money on him, but I also have a little more for you."

We arrive at the Hyatt nine minutes later. I pop out, open, and close their doors, "THUMP, THUMP!" Mark pulls out a wad of cash from his monogrammed wallet. "This is for you. I thank you for everything tonight," and hands me the third $20 bill.

"No worries, bro. My pleasure Mark."

I've made my money. It's late, and I'm ready to go home. Just one problem. I forget to turn the app off. Before I can shut the app off on my phone another ride comes in. It's hard for me to turn easy money away. The name flashes on the screen and I yell, "Freakin' Martin!"

Reaching "The Mad Hatter" again, Martin is outside doing a little song and dance looking way too happy to see me. I mumble under my breath. "Oh, brother."

"Daaaarling! You again." He dances all the way to my car and once again sits in the passenger front seat. "Oh, it is my lucky day. How was your night driving Daaaarling?"

I lower the volume on the music. "Martin, it was interesting, to say the least. Let me sum it up. I drove a gay man who offered me a blow job. I drove a drug addict into the hood for a drug deal while he was nodding in and out on his heroin high. The ride before yours was another drug-run with a john who was strapped and his geographically challenged hooker. Just another regular South Florida night. Now, here we are together again. How was your Christmas party?"

"Well, nothing compared to your night, Darling. That sounds exhilarating. My party was nothing but a bunch of ferries running around. Uggh...I'm so over it, darling."

Chuckling back, "Ferries Martin. You better not be over it because that is your sexual partner of choice. That's what you have to deal with. Women are no easier."

Our eyes lock. Big mistake. He says, "In the gay community they sleep around with everyone. They are promiscuous. Everyone in that bar has slept with each other. I'm over it darling. Now daaarling, you sure you don't want that blow job now?" He slips his hand onto my thigh for a nano-second.

Immediately I remove his hand. "Yo, Martin. Don't make me whoop your ass. I don't think you're being cool. I love women, bro.

Don't let that happen again. You need to stop thinking you can turn every straight man and stop being so aggressive. If I were into dudes, which I'm not, you are an old, pervy, man who would never do it for me. I have been more than kind and respectful to you. Let's finish the night on a good note, no?"

"Darling, you're right. I'm sorry about coming on to you, but you're just such a handsome bloke. I'm jealous of that wife of yours. All the good-looking blokes are straight."

"I think that's so funny because I know women, that say all the good-looking men are gay. I'm not so sure about the man my wife thinks she has, but I do have a hell of a wife who is also stubborn as hell. She has a very bad temper. I can take it for a while. Lately, I've been blowing up back. Our marriage is falling apart and it's both our faults." I slow down to make a right-hand turn into the parking lot. "Alright, Martin. You take care, man. I hope you find what you're looking for."

Martin opens the door and steps out with a twirl. He closes the door, and in true Martin fashion, pirouettes, popping his head back into the window, "I found what I was looking for. It's not looking for me. Call me when you're ready for that blowjob." He winks at me. I throw my head back and laugh.

I drive to the Cumberland Farms at the corner to fill up my tank before heading home. My wife is in bed by 10 P.M. every night. Everyone is sleeping. I walk through the house quietly, slide the glass back door open, and kick my feet up in the adjustable lounge chair on the porch. Exhausted, I light up the last joint of the day, taking long puffs. I finish smoking and relax, watching the moon light reflect off the water.

This Sunday morning is the beginning of the end of my marriage. If I had to pick a spot, this would be it. I'll never forget it. My wife and I haven't talked all day over a salsa battle. The Dolphins are 7-7 in the NFL and still in the playoff hunt. They are playing the Jaguars in the early game. While sitting on the couch with my feet up, the broadcaster announces, *"Look at this, folks. Blake Bortles is coming in with the game tied at 7-7 in the 3rd quarter. He will try to get the Jags on the board with this drive."*

My wife strolls over, "Can we talk about tomorrow and Christmas?"

"Yes. I've been meaning to talk to you about that. What's up?"

"Well, you know we do Christmas Eve at my parents' and then Christmas Day in the morning for presents and church."

"Yes, right."

"Well, what are we doing? What's the plan?"

I drop my feet to the floor and sit up straight. "That is what I wanted to talk to you about yesterday. You know I drive full-time now. I wanted to compromise with you. I can't do both days. I was thinking about driving on Christmas Eve. Not driving at all on Christmas Day. I'm all yours on Christmas Day."

"No. I need you to take off both days. I don't want to be alone on Christmas Eve."

"O.K., look. I can drive a little Christmas Eve night and then come over. It will be after the Christmas Eve celebration, but I can be there."

She sits down next to me. "That defeats the purpose. Why can't you just not drive either day? Why can't you drive early in the day on Christmas Eve or late in the day on Christmas Day?"

"Well, because someone has to pay the mortgage. You don't help me with it. I have asked you for help so many times. Again, I don't mind busting my ass and paying the mortgage by myself, but you can't be on me about my work schedule and when I should be working or not. I don't get to choose when the rideshare business is busy. The times you want me to drive are never busy. I'm sorry. That's why we need to come to an agreement we can both be happy with."

She's staring down at her purple manicured nails, sharpened like little coffins. She looks back up and I see a world of hurt in her face. Her eyes overflowing with tears. "You're never there for me. You're never there when I need you. Why can't you just do this for me? Just these two days. Here I am going to be again with my family alone.

My husband would rather work than be with me. I always had to do things alone in my last relationship when I was with my ex-husband.

My voice raises and cracks with tension. "Why does that always have to be the narrative? How about you have your husband's back? You should say, hey guys, my husband has to work tonight, but he will be here all day tomorrow. You know, the day that actually counts? Someone has to pay this mortgage. I'm not trying to be mean, but your part time job isn't going to cut it."

Her weeping gets louder. My heart is crumbling, but I think, *"There's no way this can't make sense to her, right? It's simple math. Time plus rides equals money. Money pays the bills."*

She stands up, and I continue speaking, "Also, it's not just the two days. Remember you scheduled a trip for all of us to go to St. Augustine next weekend for New Year's? That's more time missed. When do you think I'm supposed to work?"

She covers her face with both hands. All I want to do is hug her, but I don't. Muffled through her tears, I can make out, "You don't care. You don't care about me or this marriage. That's why you have mentioned divorce. You don't care!"

This enrages me even more. I stand up and run my hands through my hair, shouting. "How can you say that? How can you say that I don't care? I buy you this townhouse when you know I can't afford it on my own. But, somehow, I'm busting my ass and getting it done. I don't bother you on your days off. You're here relaxing while I'm killing myself, right?" I begin to pace, back and forth between the couch and the sliding glass door as she cries. "I do it because I love you, but when you bring up that I don't care and it has to do with me working, I'm going to bring up your four days off a week. You want to see me more? Then help me more. We agreed prior to buying this place that you would take more hours. That has never happened. It's been over a year. The only reason I bring up divorce is because you seem constantly unhappy. I'm convinced there is nothing I can do to make you happy. I'm even trying to compromise right now, and that's not enough!"

"Well…I'm constantly working to upkeep the home. You don't help."

My voice remains stern. "I don't ask you to make dinner. I eat out most of the time alone. You usually only make enough dinner for yourself and your kids. How does that make me feel? Not even an extra plate. I don't ask you to do my laundry. As a matter of fact, I do it myself. I don't demand you clean the house. I don't do anything most machismo Spanish husbands do or expect their wives to do. I don't know what you want from me, woman!"

She becomes hysterical and loudly declares, "Love and support. That's all I want! Love and support, damn it!"

I slide over to embrace her. "I don't know what you want me to do. I don't know what else to do. I have to work."

She finally gathers herself together in my arms and the tears stop. "I have to go. I have to buy some groceries. I told my mom I would stop by and get things ready for tomorrow."

I sit back down on the couch. "O.K. I'll be here with the kids. Just gonna watch some football." She leaves my arms and returns to the kitchen wiping her eyes with tissue the whole way. Minutes later the front door shuts. I turn the TV back on and listen to the announcer, *"The Dolphins fall to 7-8 and have been eliminated from the playoff hunt by the Jags as they fall here today 17-7."*

In full couch potato mode, I watch the 4 P. M. games and then the 8 P.M. game. I fall asleep. My wife doesn't wake me. She leaves me sleeping on the couch often. This couch surfing is becoming a bad habit.

PART II : A Happy Christmas?

It's Christmas Eve morning and the roads should be busy. Driving to the trusty Cumberland Farms to fill up, I roll down the windows. I proceed to park down the street at the neighborhood park, admiring the lake and rolling one up. Strolling to the dock, I lean on the rickety brown railing, take a puff and watch the sunrise. A sudden ripple in the water draws my attention. The fish and turtles are out for an early swim and join me in my morning smoke. After finishing the blunt, I book it to the car, put on the seatbelt, and turn on the tunes. Dropping the visor to check myself in the mirror allows me time to prepare myself physically and mentally for the day ahead.

A steady flow of rides have me traveling south, ending up in Ft. Lauderdale. On average, 85% of rides head south. I have a decent morning and reach my goal. Leaving Ft. Lauderdale and hopping on I-95 my phone rings, "RING, RING, RING!"

It's my wife. I answer pleasantly believing we had come to an agreement about my holiday work schedule. "Hey, what's up?"

"Are you coming home to get ready for my parents?"

"I thought we agreed I would work tonight and be there tomorrow."

"So, you're not coming? You're making me go alone. I can't believe I'm going through this again."

"Going through what? Babe. I have to work! One of us has to pay the bills." I can feel the tension rise through the phone. The crying begins, and I feel confused.

"I knew you would do this. You care more about work than you do about me. I'm going to have to go alone because my husband would rather work."

"I'm on my way home because I'm done with the morning. At 7 P.M. I have to be back on the road. That leaves me six hours. Why does the story always have to be that your husband would rather be working? Why can't the story be my husband is out providing and he will be here tomorrow? Tomorrow is Christmas and I find that to be the more important day. That's it! It's not that hard."

She wails, "I need you. Why can't you be here for me? My anxiety is through the roof! I don't have my kids this year and I'm feeling down."

"I'll be home soon. I'll see you then. I don't know why you get like that. We always have your kids. I'll see you soon. I can't keep talking. I'm on the highway and have to pay attention." I drop the phone in the empty passenger seat and step on the gas. I'm breaking ninety, but it doesn't matter. I want to resolve this issue. I get home, park, and make my way to sit at my bed/couch in the living room.

She stomps over tough as nails and gripes, "I don't have my kids this year. I need you there tonight!"

"OK. So, if I go tonight, I don't have to be there tomorrow for Christmas? I can work tomorrow?"

She looks at me sternly. "No! I need you then also."

I look her back in the eye. "Again, you know this already. I don't get to decide when it's busy. If I did, I would work anytime and be alright. I have to work one night or the other. This is my job full-time. Can't give up both days!"

Her eyes are puffy and overflowing, "I can't understand why you can't make both. I'm your wife!"

"I don't understand what you're not getting. What you're asking for is unreasonable. Why can't you back up your husband?" I pound on my chest and say, "You never back any decision I make. You're so big on the Bible, but you're never supportive like it says. I'm trying to compromise here!"

She screams, "I don't have to be submissive to a husband if he's not leading!"

My voice raises, "I always try to lead, sweety. I am not asking you to be submissive. The problem is that you can't have two chiefs, and you're never willing to stand with me!"

She cries louder and sobs into her hands while they cover her face. "You're an asshole! You don't love me. You're never there for me. Why can't you sacrifice these two days? I'm cursed with the husbands I choose."

"I didn't call you any names," I say while squeezing the couch pillow to contain my anger. "I thought we went through this already.

You can continue to enjoy your four days off. I have to work." I run my hand through my hair and pull on a strand trying to distract myself. "There's no way around that! I'm sorry." The tears flow all the way up to the master bedroom. She closes the bedroom door and I hear the button lock click.

Laying back on the couch, emotionally drained, I think, *"I'm never going to make this woman happy. Nothing I do will make this woman happy. Maybe we are not supposed to be together."* I doze off and don't wake up at 7 P.M. per my plan. Instead, I wake up at 2:27 A.M. Christmas morning! Nobody is home. I run upstairs and throw on a black blazer over my jeans and red shirt, grab my gorilla glue gel, tighten up my hair, and what do I do next? Naturally, turn on the apps.

My first job comes in and is located only five minutes away. Once at the pickup location, I look around and find a couple outside the gate, arms crossed tight and close to their bodies wearing sweaters. The woman's hair blows wild around her face. I don't have a chance to open both doors, but I open and close the woman's door. "THUMP!" I do the usual confirmation, and this one's cute, "Mickey and Minnie?"

"That's us! Mayi?"

"Yes, sir. Headed to 346 LeJeune Rd, Miami?"

"Yes, sir."

"We are heading west so I'm going to hop on the Ronald Reagan Turnpike. Is that alright by you?"

"Yes sir. You're the Captain, but thanks for asking. We hope you're better than the last guy."

The woman chimed in, "My husband didn't mean anything by that. It's been interesting, to say the least. Thanks for having it warm in here."

"My pleasure. It's chilly out. I figured passengers would want to get into a warm car. So, you know I gotta ask. What happened with the last guy?"

I glance in the mirror. They make eye contact in the back. I ride through the Sun Pass lane and merge onto the Ronald Reagan Turnpike heading south.

"If it gets stuffy in here, let me know. Are you comfortable with seventy five on the highway?"

Mickey answers, "Yes, sir. Seventy five is fine. So far, you're better than the last guy."

Minnie leans forward and continues, "Mayi, we actually just got out of a rideshare right before you picked us up. The driver picked us up from our Christmas party, and when he was talking to us and confirming, he was slurring his words heavily and speaking very slowly. My husband thought, hey, maybe he's just slow, but when he started driving, he was all over the road. Couldn't stay in the lane. My husband turned to me and said we got to get the fuck out of this car before we die. This guy was more hammered than us. We found the first neighborhood, where you picked us up and told him we forgot our friend was having a Christmas party there. We told him we wanted to stop by, and here we are."

"Let me ask you something. Did you guys report him?"

"No. We didn't want to do that. We didn't want to hurt him with the job."

"You should have reported him. I would have. That defeats the purpose for your driver to be incoherent. I believe part of the job is to get you guys home safe. I bet you didn't think of this. What if he's the car that T-bones us later tonight? We don't know where he went. Another question. Don't you think he might go pick someone else up next and put them in danger?"

"Wow! You're right. We didn't think of any of that. Hun, I can't believe we didn't think of that."

"Well, we are probably in the clear as far as getting hit. Guys don't be shy to report a driver like that. It's in everyone's best interest."

"Yes, you're right. We will next time."

"I normally don't drive at night because of all the crazy drivers, but I fell asleep at 2 P.M yesterday. Woke up this morning wide awake and couldn't get back to bed. May as well make some extra money."

Micki says, "Yeah, why not? No plans for the Holidays?"

"Later today, I'm going to my in-law's house. We are going to do the Christmas thing there again this year. I can't wait for the food!"

I pull off the Turnpike, and after some more small talk, we arrive at their home.

"Mayi, thank you for the nice ride. It was a pleasure meeting you."

I open and close Minnie's door, "THUMP!"

"Thank you, guys. The pleasure is all mine. You have a nice night and a Merry Christmas."

I hop back in and it's a little stuffy, so I crack the windows. Leaving them behind, I get stuck at the first red light at LeJeune Road. My light turns green, but I hesitate. There's one car heading west with a red light, and they look at me, probably wondering why I haven't crossed yet. I do not know why I didn't just go through the light. There is no car behind me. I'm sitting at my green light for seven seconds at 3:30 A.M when something catches my attention out of the corner of my eye. I look left, and see a black box truck, a real old GMC heavy-duty metal truck with its headlights off booking about ninety. I think, *"There's no way he's stopping. He's running this light."* Sure enough, he runs the light. I would have been severely injured, if not dead. I believe God intervened. The truck would have T-boned my driver's side.

God wasn't done saving my life. He saved my life twice in one shot. The shock I'm feeling is so paralyzing that I still have not moved my car. I am quickly checking around, verifying all my body parts are intact and I really survived, thanking God, when all of a sudden, screeching tires jar me, "EEER…EEER…EEER!" A silver Mitsubishi from the same direction comes flying after the box truck, speeding on the wrong side of the road, heading west on the eastbound lane. Still frozen at my green light I watch the car cut into the right side of the road at the intersection and almost flip. Both passenger tires clip the median. If the first vehicle wouldn't have hit me at the intersection, the second one would have surely succeeded. I watch blue and red lights flicker past. *"Hmmm, I'm gonna make this right."*

Finally able to move, I make a right turn and stop a quarter mile down the road at a Checker's. The man in the box truck is on the ground, handcuffed. In the parking lot the silver Mitsubishi headlights are shining from afar in a parking spot with the engine running. I'm on the curb westbound, and holler at the officer. "Sir, that silver car over there was racing with him! He was on the wrong side of the road, and they both could have killed me!" The Mitsubishi driver peels out and one of the officers takes off, his Crown Victoria in hot pursuit. From there, I don't know what happened to these clowns. It's been a weird night.

I'm really not in the mood to drive, but complete a few more rides anyway. I am between rides, in the middle lane, when a red Civic in the right lane decides to cut across three lanes to get to the left turn lane. "Jesus!" I yell. This is it for me. I'm done. I don't normally do nights, and it's been too crazy already on the streets. Driving home, and the sun is not out yet. Looking up, the quarter moon is filling the sky. It follows me home to the tune of House music on the radio and helps to keep my eyes open. Rolling into the driveway, relieved to see on the clock that it is not 6 A.M yet, I am excited to get some good shut eye before the Christmas celebration.

I wake up at 1 P.M. The house is empty again. My wife has left me again. Three solid hours pass by watching Christmas movies and crying alone. I cover my face with my hands and wipe my tears with my t-shirt. Standing up and not knowing what step to take next, I fall on my knees and pray aloud. "Lord, please help me. I don't know what to do. My marriage is falling apart. I have no clue what to do to make this woman happy. This isn't supposed to be this hard. Why can't we just be happy? I'm not even sure I'm supposed to be with her. How can she say she loves me and yet, have an issue with everything I do, or don't do? I thank you for what I have and don't. I thank you for the people you have brought in and out of my life. Lord, please forgive me for my earthly sins. In the name of Jesus Christ I pray, Amen." I throw myself back on the couch in despair. Minutes later, I get up and walk out to the porch staring out into the lake for answers.

My wife finally arrives at 6:23 P.M. She silently walks by me in the living room and neither of us acknowledges the other. Not a word. My restlessness gets the best of me and I leave to drive on Christmas Day and night, wearing the same damn thing, on an empty stomach feeling like crap. I am unsure of how we got to this place in our marriage.

Communication, or lack thereof, will tear families apart. The work week flies by, but at home it's like living in a deserted museum filled with coldness and silence. All week is spent politely ignoring each other and avoiding the same airspace. Now, with COVID-19 they say six feet apart will keep you safe. In this house I needed at least thirty feet.

Thursday, I come home in the middle of the day for my break, and my wife is sitting on the couch watching "Power" eating a slice of pizza. I prepare myself a bowl of soup and sit down next to her attempting to break the silence. "Are we still doing New Years' at St. Augustine? Am I still going? What are we doing here? Maybe you should just go with your parents. I mean, we aren't getting along and haven't even said a word to each other in four days."

She grabs the remote, pauses the show, and turns to her right to face me. "What! Are you going to leave me alone again? My husband should come with me as planned."

Smiling incredulously, "You know, you got issues. You got serious problems. How can you say I left you? You're the one who disappeared twice. You didn't even bother to wake me. You intentionally left me on Christmas."

Red and enraged by my smile she screams, "No, I do not have issues! You always try to flip things on me."

"Don't you think maybe I shouldn't go? We are a disaster right now, and I don't want us to be the reason your parent's and sister's family vacation gets ruined. We are yet to go on a successful family trip. Costa Rica, Orlando, and New York-twice!" I hold up four fingers. "Always a fight. Always a bad ending. Maybe I should stay home."

"No! My husband should be with me, I said!"

"O.K., that's fine. I will go, but I will drive my own car. Worst-case scenario, I can drive in St. Augustine and make some money."

"There you go. Always thinking about driving!" She stands up and walks to the kitchen to wash her plate without another word.

My blood boils, "You like chilling here on a fucking Thursday, right? You have that luxury. Am I fucking right? Guess you think the bills will just pay themselves." I roll my eyes, "Can't wait for Saturday." She storms upstairs. I finish my soup, clean my bowl, hurry to the door and yell, "BYE!" I can't shake the feeling that this vacation is going to be a disaster, just like every vacation we have ever taken.

Part III: Between Firm and Faithful

It's 5 A.M. Saturday, December 29th. We are driving to St. Augustine. Everything was prepared the night before. The three kids are sleeping in the backseat with our new dog Oakley. I love my Labrador puppy. I have slept more days with Oakley on the couch than with my wife since the day she surprised our household with a pet. My wife and I have not said three words to each other all morning. I let the radio play. It's early. Barely a car in sight. Dark and nothing but roadways and forests to see the whole ride up. Four hours later, still, without saying a word to each other, we arrive at our AirB&B. It's a cookie-cutter home fifteen minutes from the historical downtown district of St. Augustine, Florida.

We enter the home dragging our luggage and groceries. Pointing down the hall I direct the group, "O.K. you kids get that room and you boys take that room on the right. Your mother and I will take this room." I point at the master and then walk over to the kitchen window over the sink to peer out. "Guys, this backyard is huge with a lake. I'm going to walk around the lake and stretch out my legs. Everybody shower because we are meeting your grandparents downtown." I grab a lawn chair that was on the porch on my way to the lake and post it up a few feet from the bank. I sit down, roll up a spliff and light up. I walk the lake for a half hour before returning to the Air B&B. "Hey, you guys ready? We gotta go."

"Yes, Mayi. We all took showers and got dressed. Let's go." My wife talks to me for the first time in six days.

"Kids, get in the car. Let's go." The ride is just as quiet as the ride up. Mom and I are the wind chill factor making the car ice cold. The kids can feel it. The silence is deafening, but I zone out driving. Thank you, Mary Jane of the Lake. My wife and I are yet to really talk. We are about to see her family. Things are about to get more awkward.

We meet up with my seven in-laws ranging in age from seven up to sixty years old. All immediately know what's up because my wife and I wear it on our sleeve and it is an ugly outfit they have seen us both wear before.

Her dad Antonio is tall and skinny with horn-rimmed glasses. Reminds me of "Where's Waldo" without the red and white sweater. An open, likeable Christian. Her Venezuelan mom was orphaned when her parents passed away in a tragic accident. She is also Christian but not nearly as likeable. Sometimes we don't see eye to eye because of her quick rush to judge others. I see where my wife gets her Cold War tactics from.

Our two families couldn't be more different and everyone on both sides of the aisle noticed at our wedding. My family was dancing and ready to celebrate all night long, as is our Cuban culture. Her mom shooed the guests out at 10 P.M.

I love her sister Maria and Maria's husband, Otis. My only issue with them is that if it's not their way, you probably won't see them at all.

Antonio embraces me in a tight hug and asks, "Hey, Mayi. How are you? How are you guys?"

Holding him close, I whisper back. "Hey Antonio. Not good man. As I'm sure you know. We really haven't said a kind word since Christmas."

"Yeah. I heard. Hope you guys can kiss and make up here so we can all have a beautiful time. You know I love you. Do you want me to say something? I can talk to her for you."

"I know that you do. No. Let her be. Maybe we make up; maybe we don't. I don't know, but as usual, we haven't spoken."

"That's bad. I'm sorry to hear that. You know if there is something I can do, I will."

"I know. I know you love us and want it to work. I know you would do anything for your daughter and me."

The children are excited to see each other. We walk the historic downtown district. St. Augustine is full of rich traditions. It is the first settled city in the U.S. Roaming the old brick streets, I notice the re-stored school light posts and traditional Spanish colonial architecture. There is a random cannonball at every corner. The bronze statue in the Main Square of explorer Ponce de Leon is towering over me and stands eleven feet high on a six-foot high granite. It depicts him with his right hand raised and pointing out in front of him. His left-hand rests on his left hip, and he is dressed in 16th century Spanish attire, including a helmet with a feather plume and boots that extend above the knee.

The boys and I run over for a quick photo op with Ponce De Leon. Peeking around the statue, I can't help but notice the Bridge of Lions to the east. It's named for the magnificent lion sculptures that adorn it named Firm and Faithful. This is the part of the day I enjoyed, watching the boys laugh and play while the girls gossip, taking in the sites as a family.

Antonio yells, "Hey guys I'm hungry. Let's go eat!"

I respond, "That's a great idea. I'm starving, too!"

Otis says, "Let's go eat at the Cuban restaurant Columbia!"

The boys, "Ah, we aren't really hungry. Can we eat later?"

The ladies, "Boys, you're eating now with us as a family. Then, you can go play."

Smiling, I bust their chops, "I eat Cuban all the time, but I will for you guys today."

We enter the restaurant Columbia and they seat the twelve of us on the second floor. This would foreshadow my Last Supper with the group.

"Sir, I'll have the Pan con Bistec without mayonnaise, please."

My wife orders, "Lechon Asado with an Arnold."

The waiter asks confused, "Ma'am, what's an Arnold?"

"Duh, an Arnold Palmer." She laughs in his face, "Lemonade and sweet tea."

"We only have pink lemonade here, ma'am."

"Guess that will have to work." She hands the menu back to him without a please or thank you.

The rest of the family place their orders. Everyone cross-talks to each other over lunch except for my wife and me. After we finish eating, we continue roaming the square. Everyone notices we are not talking, but for the sake of us, they don't say anything. We keep it moving and are enjoying the sites when we come up to Castillo de San Marcos. This is the oldest masonry fort in the continental U.S. and the focal point of the town. St. Augustine is over 315 years old, as old as this marriage has made me feel.

At 7 P.M we are in front of Hippos Ice Cream Shop. "Hey, guys, I read about this place. This ice cream is all-natural. Give me a minute. I want to get a bar. Hey, bud! You want one?" I ask my son.

"Sure Papi. Get me a strawberry."

Everyone follows me inside except for my wife. We all buy ice cream. I sneak up on my wife who is waiting outside. There is an ice cream treat in my hand, hidden behind my back, with her name on it. She turns maroon and cracks a forgiving smile as she accepts the bar from me.

"Thank you, Papi."

"You're welcome, baby." I lean in and give her a kiss. Everyone walks out and sees us.

"Awww...Yay...It's about time...That's what we like to see."

We continue our stroll hand in hand. It's getting late and chilly when Otis states, "We're going to Jacksonville tomorrow. We should all go."

"Sounds good to me. In that case, I think we are gonna head out. I need to rest if I'm driving more tomorrow." My wife and I say good-bye to everyone.

Her dad leans over and says, "Thank you." I nod in acceptance, give him a hug, and we take off to our AirB&B. When we arrive at the AirB&B, everyone is so tired that we shower and immediately go to sleep.

The next day I help get the children ready in the morning while my wife is making breakfast. We meet in the kitchen. "Babe, what's for breakfast?"

"Papi, I made scrambled eggs and waffles. Thought I'd keep it easy on vacation. Can you get the O.J. from the fridge, please?"

"Got it. Good call. Is there anything else you need me to do?"

"No Papi. Everything else is done. Thank you. Kids, come on! Food's ready!" We all sit down at the round kitchen table and lock hands. I pray aloud.

"Dear Lord, thank you for what you have given us and for what you haven't. Thank you for the people you have brought in our lives and the people you have taken out. Lord, I pray in the name of Jesus Christ that you forgive us for our earthly sins. Lord, I know that no matter what happens yesterday, today, or tomorrow that you are faithful and your promise is kept. We thank you for blessing us with this wonderful food and this time together. We ask that you protect us, our friends, and family and those we don't know. Save those who seek saving. Help those who seek help and protect those who need it. Lord, again thank you for all you do. In the name of Jesus Christ, we pray, and everyone said-"

"Amen."

My little twelve-year-old asks, "Papi, pass the eggs, please?"

"Here you go, bud."

My wife's younger son asks, "Mami, can I have only waffles? I don't want eggs today."

"Sure. You O.K baby? You love eggs."

"I'm just not that hungry."

"Well, have three waffles then."

He gets excited and opens his eyes wide, smiling, "O.K." The cling and clang of plates being passed around is the only sound you hear.

The kids take off to play in the humongous backyard. The wife and I sit down on the couch and watch TV until her parents and sisters' family arrive. We keep the conversation light. They are raring to go. The kids meet us at the door, and we hop in two cars. Jacksonville is forty-five minutes away. We all have our long sleeves on because the skies are grey and murky. We wander by Jacksonville Bay, Jaguar stadium, and downtown Jacksonville. The kids are running around while we savor the sites downtown. Antonio suggests, "Let's go to the beach."

The girls respond, "That sounds great!"

When we run up on the beach, the winds are stronger than expected. My wife's hair is blowing all over her face. "Papi, hug me. I'm cold."

Naturally, I hug my wife. "This wasn't such a great idea. It's not that chilly, but this wind is killing me." Moving her hair away from her face, "The fog sucks, too. I want to go."

"Yeah. Me, too."

My wife shouts at her family. "Hey, guys. You know we got the AirB&B, so we have a lot of room. Why don't you guys come over and hang out for dinner?"

"Sure. O.K. Let's get out of here. This stinks anyway." The group agrees.

We head back to our cars, picking up our pace faster and faster as the temperature gradually drops. We stop at Publix Grocery store on the way back to pick up some items to cook dinner. Once we arrive at the AirB&B, we spend time in the kitchen preparing the food we bought. We eat as a family, hang out, and talk. Some watch TV. My wife and I are actually getting along.

Antonio stretches and yawns. "Aauuh! Guys, time to go. We got a big day tomorrow. We will be here early in the morning."

New Years' Eve morning my clothes are hanging up ready in the bathroom closet. Her family is already here. My wife walks into the bathroom where I am showering and after brushing her teeth asks, "Papi, what are you wearing?"

"Babe, I pulled out dark blue jeans and the white hoodie with baby blue sleeves."

"Papi, wear the long sleeve V-Neck."

I'm not sure how, but this moment forever alters the rest of our existence.

"Nah, Babe! I'm wearing what I have out. Not changing."

She huffs and puffs and with a serpent's tongue spits, "What is wrong with you? What's with the attitude? I'm tired of your attitude."

"What are you talking about? I don't have an attitude. I'm just telling you I'm not changing again."

She waves her toothbrush in the mirror and points the head at me in the reflection, "Yeah, but what's with the attitude? I'm tired of it."

"Again, what are you talking about? If anything, you're the one with the damn attitude. I'm just telling you what I'm wearing. Why is everything such a problem?"

"See, there it is again. You always have an attitude with me for anything. I'm tired of it." She shoves the toothbrush in her toiletry bag, looks again in the mirror, and begins fixing a stray hair with her fingers.

Drying off with my towel furiously I blow up. "You know what? I'm tired of your attitude. Always blaming me for everything. Complaining and thinking I'm the cause of all the problems. I'm tired of it. All I did was tell you what I was wearing! All you do is start fights with your temper." I squeeze the tooth paste so hard that it squirts over the edge of my toothbrush and onto the tile.

After brushing my teeth, I grab my hair gel and begin styling my hair when she shouts, "You always have to get the last word in, huh. You think you're always right!"

I storm out to the living room. "Ugggh! Here we go again!"

Antonio stands up and wanders over from the kitchen. "Mayi, what happened? What's going on? It was such a beautiful day yesterday."

"Antonio, your daughter's temper is getting on my last nerve. I really don't want to talk about it if you don't mind. I'm not trying to be a jerk, but I'm not sure I should be talking to you about your daughter."

Antonio walks into the bedroom to speak privately with his daughter. A few minutes later he emerges making his way to the front door. His daughter follows silently behind him. Antonio says, "Let's go, guys. We got a lot to do today before tonight."

We get in our cars and take off for downtown St. Augustine. Once there, we hop on the trollies and check out the sites. We hop off at the Fountain of Youth and walk around. We hop back onto the trolley and visit the old jail. My wife speaks to everyone but me. I think, *"This has got to be so awkward for her parents. I feel like I'm a prisoner. I can only imagine how they feel."* They try to make small talk with us but we both shun it.

Antonio says, "Guys, let's be happy. It's New Year's Eve."

Sarcastically I reach my hands to the sky and scream "YAY!" My wife stays quiet. After we spend a miserable morning and afternoon together, we return to the AirB&B at 7 P.M. After showering, I lay on the couch and turn on the TV. My wife sits next to me on a love seat.

"Mayi, I'm going to a fair with my parents for New Year's. That's what we are doing tonight in case you want to come."

"I don't want to go. Why would I want to go? I don't feel like ruining the rest of the time your parents are here. I think you guys should go as a family." I sit up, put my face between my hands, roll my fingers down my eyes and gaze at her. "I think I'm going to stay. We haven't been talking to each other, and I don't feel like doing this tonight. I feel bad enough about the day."

"You make this a bigger deal than it is. You can just come."

"I don't think you make a big enough deal about your behavior. We both show our anger and don't know any other way. I'm not going through that again. If anything, we should be staying here and trying to work this out as a family. Here. Together. Not out celebrating. It's not a good idea."

"Well, we are meeting my sister there."

"You guys have a good time." She walks away.

Her parents arrive at 9:30 P.M. Antonio sits next to me on the couch and her mom joins her in the other room.

Antonio leans in. "Hey, Mayi, you coming? You don't look dressed for the weather."

"No, Antonio. I don't want to be the reason tonight is awkward again. The kids are there with Otis already. Just let them know I don't feel well. I think you should go and have a good time. We have solved nothing here. I'm good."

"I get it. O.K., Mayi."

Antonio stands up. "Ladies, you ready? Let's go! It's getting late." The ladies gather in the living room. I can see from my wife's eyes that she has been crying. Her mother won't even look at me.

"Happy New Year Antonio." By 9:47 P.M., I'm on my knees crying again just like Christmas Day. My marriage is broken.

"Dear God, thank you for everything you have given me and everything you haven't. Thank you for everyone you have brought in my life and taken out. In the name of Jesus Christ, I pray that you forgive me for my earthly sins. Lord, I need your help. We are falling apart. I'm falling apart. Please help me." I cry out, "I'm trying. I really am. I don't know what else to do. Please give me a sign. Give me a sign of what I'm supposed to do. I'm sorry that I have mentioned divorce, but I don't know what else. I'm giving her a way out. She's never happy. Lord, I beg you! Please help me! Maybe it's me. If so, help me to be a better man. Don't give up on me. I won't on you. Lord, I love you, I thank you. In the name of Jesus Christ, I pray, Amen."

I pull myself together and decide to get out of the house. I turn on my apps. It's surging with big-time premiums all night. I'm going to spend New Year's with strangers in my car. The evening is mostly a blur. What I do remember is a ride to Jacksonville and a ride back. I drove from 10:15 P.M. to 2 A.M. and made $340. Really good night, normally. I return to an empty AirB&B. Not sure if my wife came back at night, or in the morning, and too drained to notice or care. Cuddling with Oakley gives me solace. New Year's Day morning my wife appears. We prepare to leave after an uncomfortable breakfast, riding home with a heavier tension than even the ride up. Rather than ride in silence, I turn the music up louder, counting down the hours for this trip to end. I have spent Christmas Eve, Christmas Day, and New Years' Eve alone.

We finally arrive home and unpack all the bags, backpacks, and suitcases. We shoo the kids into the shower and lay them down for the night. I'm downstairs watching TV. My wife comes downstairs, sits next to me, and does what I can't stand. She takes the remote and turns off the TV. Maybe to me the show was something important, but she doesn't care. This is her game. I keep my cool and say, "Make it quick. I don't want to do this tonight. Go ahead, but I already see where this is going."

"Mayi, we either have to do marriage counselling or get divorced. This isn't working and it's not fair to the kids."

"For once, we agree on something!"

Oakley   Townhome

DAY 3.

REVELATIONS AND LESSONS

Part I: Revelations

"I cannot believe you left me alone at an AirB&B in Clearwater four hours away from home!" Roaring into my phone and pacing, "This is what I get for not driving my own car. This is becoming a habit. It's 9:30 A.M. If you're not here by noon, I'm leaving! I'll take a rideshare back!"

"You're crazy. I'll be there. Just wait. I'm having breakfast with my parents and my sister."

My blood is boiling, and the mercury in my mental thermometer is about to burst through the phone. "Do you know what it feels like to wake up to an empty strange place? You're so damn selfish! You didn't even try to wake me. If you're not here at noon, I'm telling you, I'm outta here! Thanks for a great Labor Day! I know you did this on purpose! You knew I wanted to leave this morning after the way last night ended."

"Last night was not my fault! I wasn't feeling well, and you got mad again."

"Dude you were ruining everyone's night with the pity party. It's not that you're not feeling well, it's the attitude that comes with it. All I asked was for us to leave and not ruin the time for others. You took offense to that. Listen I'm not doing this now. Be here by twelve!"

I set off at a sprint collecting all my belongings. Shoving shorts, jeans, shirts inside my orange carryall; not stopping until my toothbrush and gel were accounted for. Too heated in the moment, I want to pray but can't. Swear words flood my mind. Running out of insults I begin taking deep breaths. *"Mayi you can't change the situation. Calm down. Relax. Relax Mayi. Nothing you can do right now."*

Hangry for breakfast, my grumbling stomach leads the way to the kitchen to scramble some eggs and swipe jam on toast. Sitting depressed at the kitchen table, staring at the wall clock, minutes disappear like sand draining slowly through an hourglass.

Twelve-thirty strikes and I order my rideshare. The app connects me to a driver named John and I call him. "John this is Mayi. This is a long ride. Want to make sure you're up for it. We are heading to the east coast to Royal Palm Beach. It's at least three to four hours."

"Mayi let's rock and roll baby!"

"That's what I like to hear John. You the man. Will you be here in seven minutes?"

"Yes sir!"

"Thank you, John. See you soon." John picks me up at 12:43 P.M. Still no sign of my wife. John is a short Caucasian man with a southern accent and a goatee.

We head out to the east coast. "Mayi you mind if I vape?"

"No John. It's cool. I'm probably going to take a nap anyways."

"Thank you. I appreciate it because it is a long ride." He slips the pen between his lips and tugs at the wiry hairs of his goatee, puffing away.

"Yeah, no worries." I lay back and stare out the window.

What a role reversal. John looks in his rearview mirror. "Hey if you don't mind me asking, what brings you to Clearwater for such a long trip?"

I smile, "John that's a loaded question. You sure you want the answer?"

John smiles, "Hit me!"

"Well John I'm never going to see you again so I'm going to un-load on you." We both laugh. "I came with my wife for vacation with her family. It's so weird. We can't go on one successful vacation from start to finish. Last night at dinner-" My cell buzzes.

"Give me a moment John. That's her."

My wife asks, "Hey where are you?"

"I left. I told you I was going to. Man, I even waited until twelve forty. You're calling me now at one seventeen. I left."

"You're such an asshole. Now I have to drive my car back all alone with my kids. You didn't have to do that. It didn't have to end this way."

"You should have thought about that when you left me there or when you didn't come back by twelve thirty."

"I was eating with my family asshole. I can't control how fast or slow the place was."

"Exactly! You were eating with your family and where was I? You could have excused yourself and said I have to get back to my hus-band. Light bulb, you could have woken me up to go with you. Listen, I'm in the rideshare. We can do this when we get home. The way you speed, you will probably beat me there anyway."

"I can't believe you."

"Believe it. Talk to you at home." The call disconnects.

A text immediately beeps in from Antonio. "-*Mayi, I can't believe you left. It didn't have to be this way. Why would you do that?-*"

I text him. *"-You're right. It didn't!-"* He never texted back, ever again. I throw my phone next to me on the car seat fed up.

"So, John let's see here. Where was I? Oh yeah, we are here on a little vacation. Everything was fine until last night's dinner. We came because we thought after nine months of counseling that we could handle going on vacation together. John, I spent Christmas, Christmas Eve and New Year's Eve alone! Well, with strangers anyway, driving them around all night, just like you do."

"Awesome! Fellow driver. You do pretty good over there?"

"Yeah. I made sixty one thousand last year driving full time. Subtract five thousand for gas and maintenance. I don't drive the crazy hours. Maybe thirty eight to forty seven hours any given week. Do everything smarter not harder. No sixty hour work weeks for me. I come from a numbers background." John is doing the sixty-five speed limit. My wife drives fast when she is angry. She will definitely beat me home.

He glances in the rearview mirror and says, "Wow! That is pretty good!"

"Yeah. It's hard to want to work for anyone else. Don't like managing other people and being responsible for their work either. Just leads to me going back over their work and tweaking it a bunch to get it right. So, anyways John, to make a long story short, she leaves me this morning in the AirB&B for three hours. This isn't the first, or second time. She just leaves and doesn't say a word. I'm over it. So, I left. I'm not sure we are making it through this one. She has started going out with her co-workers a lot after hours. It's been happening more and more often. Last time the "co-workers" bit ended with a cop putting hand cuffs on her at his house. She works with his wife. She didn't really understand the significance of the flirting there, or at least acted like she didn't. Wasn't too fond of that. He ended up leaving his wife a little thereafter, too. I'm usually not jealous, but I think this relationship has completely unraveled."

"Dude I'm sorry to hear that."

"You know it happens. It's been a while coming. Thought we were getting better though. Guess sometimes people just work in cycles. Thanks for letting me vent. I'm gonna take a nap."

"I'll let you know when we are there." John turns the radio down and switches from Donna Summer to soft jazz.

Grabbing my blue baseball cap from my bag, I slap it on my head with the bill down over my eyes and drift off. The vibration of the tires rolling across the gravel rock me along providing some peace for a bit. $239 dollars later we arrive at my parents' house where my car and Oakley await. Thankfully, my parents are not home so I rush in, grab Oakley and her toys, and put her in my car. I missed her so much. Her head is hanging out the half open window, white hairs flying. Her tongue catches wind while she looks around excitedly for the source of the odors that only she can sense.

We arrive to a full, yet eerily silent house. Oakley rushes out of the car to scratch at the front door. My wife is in her pajamas sitting in the living room playing on her cell phone. The lights are all off. She already put the kids to bed. We do not speak, and I head up to take a shower. While toweling off, the reflection in the mirror reveals my wife is sleeping in the middle of our bed. Couch it is. While rolling a joint up for some "Me" time, Oakley cuddles with me on the couch. Dogs truly share unconditional love.

"ERR…ERR…ERR!" The 7 A.M. alarm sounds. The morning unfolds as yet another abnormal, normal morning. ESPN highlights run on the TV in the living room. My wife gets her kids prepared for the day and drives them to school. Upon returning, she heads straight upstairs without acknowledging my presence, leaving me no choice but to follow her and resolve this once and for all.

The "Cold Shoulder Game" that we play for weeks will not be tolerated anymore. I'm going to apply all the skills we have learned from the counseling we completed. After fifteen sessions, including watching "Love and Respect" by Dr. Emerson for ten weeks, and other helpful material, I am hopeful we can communicate positively.

Clicking off the TV, I follow her upstairs and sit at the foot of the bed. My wife is reading a book, lying down with her torso up against the wooden headboard. I lean towards her, "I don't want to drag this out like every other fight. What is going on? I know something is going on with you. You haven't been the same for a while now. I thought things were going pretty well until this weekend, but I could sense it."

She closes her book and makes eye contact. "Look…I'm going to be honest with you." She tears up. "I haven't felt the same for a long time now. I feel that I have no more love for you. I don't have any more love to give you. Even through the nine months of counseling I haven't been able to shake this feeling that you're this malicious man with evil intent." She looks down at her hands fiddling her fingers and looks back at me, "An evil man that purposely hurt me and my kids."

My heart drops to my feet and skips madly. "Wow! Ya know, you have always thought bad of me. Why did you marry me if you felt this way? Why would you marry someone you think is evil?" She sobs uncontrollably. "I'm your damn husband and you always think I'm out to get you and your kids. I treat them the same, except I can't be all over them, like I am all over my son. I'm sorry. I would think you would be more appreciative and understanding that I respect your daughter's and son's space. They have a father. I'm always there to help. I pick them up. I drop them off. Try to be a good stepdad. I go to work and come home. Gym when we can make it. Church, work, home. That's what I do." Tears escape from me as well. The pain is gushing out of both of us. She grabs a tissue from the night table next to her, trying to get her crying under control.

She screeches, "I've tried! I tried to suppress this feeling. It was like I thought my feelings didn't matter. I tucked them deep away for the marriage, for the kids. I thought I didn't matter anymore. I thought I could do it for God. But it's too hard. You're right!" She cups her head in her hands and sobbing declares, "We need to get a divorce."

Tasting my salty tears falling uncontrollably over my lips, the truth stings me, "I never knew you felt that way. Why would you think your feelings didn't matter? Everything I have done has been for you and this family. How can you feel that way? I'm not trying to invalidate your feelings, but I just don't understand." This conversation is not what I thought it would be.

She doesn't end there, saying, "You always have to prove your point that you're right. You always have to get the last word. You make me look bad in front of my family. They want nothing to do with us as far as vacation. You always leave. You abandon! You run away from the situation. You manipulate and twist things. There is nothing left. I have nothing left. I tried. We tried. God knows I tried." She explodes in agony. "I can't! I can't do this anymore!"

I stand up, "I only prove points because even when you're dead wrong, you still think you're right. You can never apologize. You say I make you look bad in front of your family? Wow! You make yourself and me look bad to your family. Who leaves who behind? When we argue I don't abandon you. I leave to blow off steam and give each other some space. I'm doing what we learned. I either go to the lake or maybe grab a beer or two at Old Key Lime and then I come home."

Not wanting to prove her point, I sit back on the edge of the bed. "Unfortunately when I come home, I am greeted with a new tug of war. I'm ready to make up. You're not. Then, you're ready to make up and I'm not. Next it's the cold shoulder bullshit again."

I slap my hand on the mattress. "Why would I manipulate anything when you have admitted you cause 98% of our fights? What's your excuse? Anxiety made you do it. You shouldn't be losing your temper. If you have nothing left, no love for me, then we should get a divorce." My eyes start overflowing again accepting defeat.

She wipes her eyes with the back of her palms sniffling. "I just don't see us coming back from this. Too much has been done. Too much damage with me and my family. I don't think I can be the same with you. Before we hate each other, or do something we regret, we should divorce. I think it's best." She buries her face in a throw pillow.

"I mentioned divorce numerous times before and that is the mistake I'll have to live with. I accept that. I really don't want to get divorced, but I do think it's the best option. Your parents know all of our problems and you know that's not healthy. I don't go back to my parents. They don't know anything. Looking at your parents is hard because I love your dad so much. I didn't think you have been in this marriage with me for a while now and it shows. It shows in our communication. It shows in the bedroom. You started going out on Friday nights long ago. You started living a separate life. You changed."

I choke up and can barely get the rest out. "I guess there's no way around the fact…the fact…oh my…that you have lost your love for me and I'm tired of hearing you tell me to leave." I lash out through my tears. "I can't believe I'm going through this again. I believe you were here with me for security for you and your kids. Thought that for a while now. I totally believe that. It all makes sense now. Thinking back to the day we talked about your lease being up and you looking for a place, I should have known, but it didn't hit me."

She says, "I don't think that's true. I'm sorry you feel that way. I'm sorry." Her voice cracks. "I can't hide how I feel anymore. You don't have to leave right away but you should. What are we going to do about the house?"

"Give me a sec." I stand up and grab a tissue from the bathroom and sit back at the foot of the bed. "Um we can sell it, or you said you wanted it right?"

"Yes. I want it. This is my home."

"Then that's that. We won't sell it and you can cash me out. I have told you this didn't feel like home to me. It was never my home. This has always been your home and I'm not looking to put a single mom with kids on the street. I'll give it to you. Just cash me out. I'm a simple guy and want to live a simple life and be happy."

"What about counseling tonight?"

"I think we should go. We owe it to the counselors. We can thank them for the help and time they have offered us and make them aware of our decision. We owe them that."

"OK. Then I'll see you at seven. I'm going to get ready to run some errands. I'm glad we could have this talk like adults."

"Yeah, me too." We stand up and give each other a kiss and a long hug. We don't want to let go of this embrace knowing this may be the last time that we feel each other's skin. It's for a good minute, but it feels like time was sped up. We both tear up again. I give her another kiss on the cheek and wipe her tears. Nothing more is said.

Feeling lost and beat up, I head to the shower to think. I throw my hands up next to my shoulders, holding myself away from the wall with the water running down my head and neck and cry out, "God why?" Knowing the answer. "Why does it hurt so much? Why me? Why again?" Pride, ego, wrath, gluttony, karma. I fall to my knees crying with the hot water running down my back. "Please God help my aching heart. Help me get through this. I know you will, and I need you NOW!" Never blaming God, blaming myself, but constantly asking for his help. I breath in through my nose and "Aaah," release the air through my mouth, trying to contain all the overwhelming feelings and thoughts. Breathing again through my nose and "Aaah," out through the mouth calms me and provides me the strength to get back up. The shower water is spraying down my face meeting my tears. My eyes are closed, my agonizing heart won't let me control all the sounds and yelps that escape. "Ehhh…Aaah…Waaa…Waaa…!" The feelings of emptiness, pain, and failure take hold. Two hours of self-loathing pass by stuck like mold to the shower because I don't want to face what lays ahead. My upside-down future awaits outside of this shower. There is no way I'm in any shape or form to speak with people and be cheery. Instead of working I spend the day with Oakley and binge on Netflix.

Later that day we meet the married couple who kindly volunteered to lead our sessions. The four of us sit at the table and open with a prayer. I begin, "Edward, Conny, it's with regret that we decided to get divorced. We both came to that decision. It's been constant bickering and fighting and I'm convinced her purpose in my life was to bring me closer to God."

My wife chimes in. "Yeah, guys we are just not getting along. You know some of the issues Conny."

Conny replies, "There's nothing we can do? That's the final decision? That's what you guys are set on doing?"

Answering for the both of us, "Conny we think that's best. She's not in love with me anymore. She can't shake her feeling that I'm this evil person. It's best."

Edward and Conny look at each other in shock. Edward says, "Well, it's your decision. We don't agree or stand by it, but we respect it. We will always be here for you if you need anything. We will pray for you."

I reply, "Thank you. I appreciate that. More than you know."

We stand up, give Ed and Conny hugs and leave. In the driveway my wife asks, "Are you coming home or going to work?"

"I'm going home. I'm in no mood to work and it's nighttime."

"O.K. see you there."

The whole month of September is spent moping around the house and avoiding work. I have never been this low before in my life. I sit around and watch crime scene investigation reruns all day long. I'm growing a beard and discovered my chin hairs are salt and pepper colored and very itchy. Until you experience a divorce, you will never understand the roller coaster of emotions. All the good, bad, and unwelcome feelings run through your bones and negativity pumps in your veins.

My newest ex nudges me. "Hey, you gonna go to work this week? You haven't moved from that couch in three weeks."

"Aaah, I'll see how I'm feeling. Not sure I feel like dealing with people right now. I might say the wrong thing. My head is not there. I'll see. Maybe just pull some Bitcoin for this month."

"You can't let this get you like this. You can't let it affect you and get you so down. Do you suffer from depression or something? Do you need to see someone? Maybe speak to someone?"

"I don't suffer from depression, but I'm sure this counts for something that can cause severe depression in someone. I'll be fine. I'm just in a funk. I'm sure I'll break out of it soon."

"I gotta go. See you later I guess."

My biggest move of the day consists of making my way to the pantry to grab a new bag of white cheddar popcorn. A woman has never affected me this much in my life. I have stayed away from everyone except Oakley and an occasional visit to Ricky Smalls. Needing to break the cycle, I call my Argentinian friend Malco. We met fifteen years ago at the gym. I could use some of his strength.

"Malco it's Mayi. Bro I need to get out of here. A change in scenery will be good for me. I think being here is depressing the crap out of me. I have to get out."

"Come bro. I got that extra room you can use. You should've left a long time ago. We can work out the numbers when you get here. Dale, come."

"Bro, thank you. I only need one month. In one month, I'll be back on my feet."

"Dale, come. You know you can stay as long as you need."

"Dale, thank you bro. I'll be there tonight."

This part was very difficult. I draw the energy to walk upstairs and start to pack. The kids are at school. My wife is at work. Running into the 'love box' I made her as a gift years ago causes me to stop. I run my fingers over the wooden lid with intricate carvings built with my own hands. The memory box held our wedding rings. My face turns red, a rush of heat hits me. I go back to packing and vow not to stop again. Crying and packing, I hurry because I got to get the hell out of dodge before completely falling apart. Sitting at the dining table one last time, I write a quick note and leave it on the table. *"Out of the 24k we have saved, I'm leaving you 16k and taking 8k. That should be more than fair and plenty."*

Standing at the porch I hug Oakley tight. "I'm gonna miss you the most mamita." While looking at the lake I struggle with letting Oakley go. We have such a bond. So many nights sharing a couch. She slept on my head, my belly and feet. I look up to the sky. "God, I ask that you find a way. You find a way to get me through this damn it. I'm begging you!" I give Oakley one more hug and kiss, rubbing our noses together and holding her beautiful furry face against mine. "I love you girl. I love you more than you will ever know. You don't know it, but you have helped me through some very tough times. God, I love you mama!" I let her go. Hustling to the car I take one last look before driving away from the only home I have ever had.

On the ride to Malco's, I laugh and cry, pounding the steering wheel, remembering the early days, contemplating the days ahead, and feeling the huge weight of uncertainty that looms. No music. Thinking of all the reasons to stay causes me to tear up again. Thinking of all the valid reasons to leave gives me strength to move on knowing it's the right choice. I pull up to Malcos ten minutes later and take a few minutes to compose myself. I get out, pop the trunk and ring Malco's doorbell. Once he helps me get settled, we sit down and share a beer at the dining room table.

I sigh. "Malco thank you for the help bro. Mira, I only need one month bro. One month and I will be back on my feet and out of here."

"Mayi bro, you can stay here as long as you want. I'm not going to charge you if you're only staying for one month."

"Oye bro. I appreciate it. You're here with your wife. I'm not going to intrude. You know my rule. Don't have another dude in your home when you have a woman. Let me pay you $350 for the month instead of nothing. That will help me and you."

"Dale, perfect."

"Bro, I'm exhausted. I'm going to go to bed."

"Dale, we can talk tomorrow or later this week. Here's a key."

"Gracias."

I slide out of my chair and leave the round dining table, reach my room and close the door behind me. Falling to my knees and leaning over the side of the queen size bed I bow my head to pray. "Lord thank you for everything you have given me and everything you haven't. Thank you for everyone you have brought in and out of my life. Lord in the name of Jesus Christ I pray that you forgive me for my earthly sins. I know that no matter what happens yesterday, today and tomorrow that you are faithful, and your promise is kept. God, please protect our kids and guide them. Lord help my wife and my son's mom find what they seek and ultimately back around to you. Lord help me through these trying times. I may not understand your plan, but I know everything is for a reason. Send me some signs. Show me. I need to get out of this rut. In the name of Jesus Christ please forgive me for my earthly sins. In the name of Jesus Christ I pray-" I have always done the signs of the cross, head, heart and shoulders,- "Amen!" Emotionally drained, I knock out quickly. I don't work for another two weeks and instead hit my Bitcoin account one last time.

I'm lying in my foreign bed, staring at my foreign alarm clock in the mid-afternoon. The October sun tries to break through my closed blinds. "RING, RING, RING!"

I answer, "Yo, what's up Rich? What's good man?"

"Mayi, I know you been down man. Let's go to Boat Yard. That's your spot. Come on. I want to go. It'll be fun. You need it."

"Let's go. I'm down tonight. I could use a night out and we haven't chilled in a minute. I got some things to do so I'll meet you there and I might go somewhere else after."

"10-4. I might chill with you after also."

"10-4 big dog. See you then!"

I have yet to get back out to drive and remain down in the dumps, staying in bed watching TV, sulking in my misery until 6 P.M. After rolling a fresh blunt I throw on a navy-blue long sleeve shirt and tuck it into soft khakis. I roll up the sleeves on my shirt and call Rich. "You about to leave?"

"Bro I already left. I'm almost in Broward."

"Leaving now man. I'll see you in forty-five. Find us a nice spot."

"Got you! See you soon!"

"10-4. Later!"

I hang up the phone, hop in the car and light up my blunt. Heading off for Ft. Lauderdale with the windows half cracked, admiring the beautiful Florida cotton candy skies, the radio plays "Old Town Road." Entering Boat Yard, it's shoulder to shoulder.

I push my way through the crowd. "Hey, excuse me…oh, thank you…sorry, coming through." Finding Rich is easy. He already has a spot at the inside bar. He's 6'4, black and skinny, my ride or die dog. I have known Rich for about eight years. Arriving at the bar I throw Rich a low-five. "Yo, what up son? How's it been man? How are you?"

"You know. Things are good but I might make some moves."

"That's my dog. Make the moves son. This place is packed with hunnies tonight."

"My man! Good seeing you bro. Glad you made it."

"Yeah bro. I figured I could use the time out. Besides I know this 51-year-old I became friends with, and she needed me to pick up a check for her last week. I brought it for her tonight and told her to meet us. She's the Old Timer who's coming with her 48-year-old friend."

"Old Timer, huh! My man! Always thinking ahead and bringing us company."

"You know women attract women!" We clown around laughing and we give each other a fist pound blow-up. Two drinks in, the Old Timer and her friend, 48-year-old approach.

"Hey what's up? How are you?" She leans in for a smooch on the cheek and a hug.

"Not too bad. Just decided to come out tonight. This is my friend Rich."

"Hey Rich! Nice to meet you." 48-year-old replies.

Rich grins, "Nice meeting you guys."

"Hey, I got that thing for ya. Here." I reach in my pocket and hand Old Timer an envelope.

"Thanks, Mayi. You did me a solid and saved me a trip up there. Ladies drink free tonight! Let me know what you want. I got you." I smile, grab her hand, and twirl her around.

"Come on! Let's go! I'll take a Tito's, seltzer water, and lime please!" We are hanging out with the two hunnies having a blast. I lean into Old Timer's ear and whisper, "Hey I made a connect at Club Vodo downtown. Why don't we all go there and then call it?"

"Let's go now because it's getting late."

"Let's go."

I pivot towards Rich. "Yo, let's go. I got a hook up at Vodo. The ladies are coming."

"O.K, I'm following you." We take a ten-minute ride over to Vodo. The line is deep, and we wait for the hunnies to arrive.

Old Timer approaches me from behind in the parking lot and whispers in my ear, "What you gonna do here big guy?"

I look over my right shoulder at her, squint my eyes and break a cocky ass smile, "You guys just follow me." I grab her hand and make our way to the V.I.P entrance.

"Hey bro. Can you get Tammy for me? Let her know it's Mayi."

"You say Mayi?"

"Yes sir."

"I don't need to get her. She put you down for four."

"Cool. Right here. Us four." I wave my hand around and again look at Old Timer. She knew what was up. They escort us to the V.I.P. section and we are dancing the whole way through. The club is deep. We arrive at our reserved spot and run into Tammy. "Oye mama. Thank you for the hook up. I appreciate it."

"Anytime Mayi. You always take care of me." I give her a peck on the cheek jump around, and dance like no one's watching.

"Yo Rich, what you think big dog? Your boy got you or what? I told you I don't play when I go! I don't go much, but when I do, I go all out!"

"Yo Mayi I'm lit bro. You hooked it up tonight. This place is jamming. We jammin' son." We give each other a low-five because he comes down to my level. We are chilling and hopping around. I lean over towards Rich and he says, "Mayi I'm ripped bro. Let's go."

"Yeah son, I'm ready!"

We say bye to Old Timer and 48-year-old. We have had a hell of a night thanks to my American Express. Rich and I parked next to each other, so we reach our cars together to head home. "Yo Rich, thanks for coming out tonight bro. I needed that."

"Nah bro. Thank you! You took care of the night. Had a blast bro. You get nuts. Damn son!"

"No other way bro. I forgot how good life can be. I'll hit you up tomorrow."

"Later bro! You OK to drive?"

"Yeah man, you?"

"Yeah bro! I'm good."

"Later!"

Heading north, approaching Yamato Road, hunger sets in. There is a gas station/ sandwich shop that makes a savory Italian hoagie. Here is where my night turns into crap. I buy my sandwich tearing it in half and devouring capicola and salami, heading west up Yamato Road. Dropping a huge piece of salami, my hunger commands me to chase the meat slice down to the floor. Next thing I know, my vehicle is tilted by the median dividing traffic. "OH SHIT!" Slamming my front drivers side tire and axle, I hit a pole, and my driver's side mirror is staring up at me from the pavement. The driver's side curtain air bag deploys "DAMN!" I look out of my window, but I can't see anything because the airbag blocks my view. My car is driving kind of weird. I pull over into a newly constructed building on the corner of Yamato Road and Congress Avenue. In a panic, my heart and mind are racing. *"Shit am I going to go to jail for this? What did I hit? How did I hit it? Where is the sandwich? Get out and leave the area. Come back for the car tomorrow. I really thought I was O.K. to drive. Shit, shit, shit."*

Leaving the car behind I jog through the bushes heading north on Congress away from the scene on Yamato Road. Shaken and disturbed a 1/4 mile down the road, I realize I left the car turned on with my keys and my wallet inside. My windows are open with a bag of

Krypto sitting in the front seat. Lightbulb pops. *"Nope! Not going back there! Not getting arrested tonight. No way I'm walking back to that car. I'm walking to my cousin Yez house."*

To distance myself further from the car, I take a longer way to my cousin's place. This made sense at the time. I left the car at 2:30 A.M. At 5:30 A.M. I reach his house. It has taken me three hours to complete a forty-five-minute walk. My thoughts are jumbled, perhaps from a concussion. *"Can't knock. Don't want to wake up the girls. Duh, go sleep on the red couch in the back. Tip toe back there and wake up before anyone notices. Best idea all night Mayi."*

I am shaken awake by a familiar face. "Mayi...wake up. Dale Mayi...entra. Sleep inside." My aunts know what's up. "Oye, que tu hiciste anoche? What you do last night? Loco!"

I roll over eyes half opened, "Ok Tia. I'll be right in. Dame un minuto."

Gotta love Cuban mothers. They are so loving. "Dale Mayi! Come on. Go sleep inside. Dale...vamos!"

I'm not going to win this fight. "OK. Tia. Ya. I'm going." I stumble inside and fall asleep on the black leather couch.

I wake up to Yez and my Father in the kitchen at 10 A.M. "Rise and shine sunshine." Yez chuckles.

"Hi Yez. Hi Dad. What are you doing here?"

"I'm working on your cousin's house down the street. What about you? How are you? You OK? You look like shit."

"Yeah, Dad I'm fine. I do need a favor from one of you or your helper. I need a ride to my car. I had to leave it at a parking lot."

"I have to go to work." Yez replies.

"I'll have my helper take you. You ready now?"

"Thank you, Dad. Love you!" I hug my dad and give him a kiss on the cheek. His helper and I leave and search everywhere I could have possibly left the car. It's nowhere to be found. I call the City of Boca Raton. "Hello my name is Mayi. Do you know if a 2019 four-door light blue Honda Civic has been towed? If so, where?"

"No sir. No car matching your description has been towed this morning."

"Thank you. I appreciate your time."

We continue to search and no luck. Knowing where I left the car and how I left it causes me to close my eyes and rub my face with both hands in frustration. *"Damn it! Where is that car?"* We call off the search and return to Yez's house to meet my Dad. "Papi let me see your phone."

"For what?"

"Damn it Papi! Give me your phone. I left my phone in the car and I can track it through Google and possibly find it. Please Papi! Let me see your phone!"

"Toma! Here, take it." He hands me his phone.

"Gracias!" I take the phone and log into my Google account tracking it to "Emerald Towing." The lady at the city could have saved us so much trouble. My Dad's helper takes me to "Emerald Towing" and agrees to wait. I greet the man at the front desk. "Hey. How are you? I think my car is here."

"Not bad. Thank you. What car is it?"

"I came to pick up the light blue Honda Civic."

His eyes pop out of his head. "Pick up? That car can't be driven. The car that was abandoned around Yamato and Congress?"

"Yes! That's the one."

"Man, I don't know what you hit, but your driver's side front axle is about four inches back from where it should be and the driver's side airbag is deployed. You have to redo the whole headliner before you can drive that car. You're more than welcome to grab your things from inside and I can tow it to a shop."

"Thanks! I'll be right back." Wandering defeated into the yard and grabbing my remaining items out of my car my mind calculates the situation. *"The weed is gone. I have four missed calls from my soon to be ex-wife. Maybe it will be minimal damage and just paying the deductible. This is going to leave me out of commission for at least another four to six weeks with repairs. How am I going to make money? Well, at least I'm not in jail. It's just a car and no one got hurt."*

The helper gives me a ride to my temporary home. Laying on the bed, wondering how my life has spiraled so far out of control, a call comes through from a toll-free number. "Hello. Can we speak to Mayi?" I sit up.

"Yes, this is him. Who's this? How can I help you?"

"I'm calling about your auto insurance. How are you today?"

"I have had better days. How can I help you?"

"Well, Mayi I am looking at your car right now and I'm sorry but I'm gonna deem it a total loss."

"What? It was just a little hit."

"No sir. Whatever you hit, you road on for a while. Destroyed the whole bottom of this car. Do you carry gap insurance?"

"Wow! I can't believe the car has to get totaled. Yes, I have gap insurance thank God."

"If you have Gap insurance you have nothing to worry about. This car has 125,000 miles in about one and a half years. You do a lot of driving."

"Yeah, I go to Boca a lot."

"O.K. I'm going to do all the paperwork I need to do. You need to get your gap insurance policy and give them a call. If you have any questions with this claim you can call me anytime."

"Thank you for handling this so quickly. You have a great day."

"Thank you. You too Mayi. It's been my pleasure."

Falling back on the bed and staring at the popcorn ceiling, *"SHIT! What am I going to do? I have no car. No way to make money. I don't know what I'm going to do."*

Looking at my phone, I remember to call my ex-wife back. "Hey. What's going on? How are you?"

"What's going on? How am I? No, how are you? I had cops here at 5 A.M. looking for you yesterday. Are you O.K? What's going on? They said they found your car abandoned last night with everything in it and the car turned on. It looked very suspicious to them, so they came by looking for you."

"What did you tell them?"

"Uh…the truth. That you don't live here anymore and that we are getting a divorce. That I have no clue where you are."

"O.K. good. I'm O.K. Just found my car. It's totaled. I don't know what I'm going to do. I haven't worked in weeks and I don't have any way to make money. I'm so screwed!"

"Oh my God. Are you O.K.? Are you hurt? Were you drunk?"

Avoiding her last question, "I'm O.K. Nothing happened. I just ran something over and damaged the whole bottom."

"You sure about that?"

"I'm sure. Look I'm not feeling well. I'll call you later or something. I gotta go."

"O.K. by Mayi."

"Bye."

I really didn't feel like talking much or explaining. I call Rich quickly. "Yo, man. I totaled my car last night."

"Yooooo, I thought you said you were good to drive."

"Yeah. I thought so, too."

"What are you going to do?"

"Rich I don't know man. When it rains it pours. I just wanted to tell you. I don't feel well. I'm going to rest. I'll talk to you later."

"O.K. bro. Hit me later."

If I was feeling some type of way before, it had nothing on how low I'm feeling now. I stay home and watch football all weekend, never leaving, and skip church. During the Sunday 4 P.M NFL games I read the gap policy and begin organizing the paperwork. A migraine sets in. It's going to take at least thirty days before the claim gets resolved.

Anything that can go wrong is going wrong. I have gone six weeks without working and bills are calling my name. The stress mounts and I want to quit life. Yet know I can't. Tuesday morning rolls around.

My inner voice forces me to get up and stop the self-pity. *"Mayi get up. Find a way to make something happen. Turn this thing around. You are stronger than this."* A simple thought pops in my head. *"I'm gonna go buy a new car. That's what I'm going to do."*

I order a rideshare to Honda on Blue Heron Blvd. in West Palm Beach. I'm waiting in the salesman office while they do what car dealerships do. He comes back from the sales managers office, sits and says, "Mayi you have a 2017 Civic, 2015 Kia Optima and a Slingshot. You're a little overextended."

"Sir I understand that. Go back over there and let him know the Civic and the Optima have been deemed total losses by the insurance companies. They are going to be paying Honda Financial and then gap covers the rest. He can double check with Honda Financial. They are already aware."

He points at the paperwork. "And the Optima?"

"Sold that car to a friend and it caught fire while he was doing a rideshare. Crazy the months I've had. Anyhow, that car has already been paid. It's just a matter of showing on my credit report. I can have that paperwork for you by the end of the month."

He returns to his sales manager and then comes back and sits down. He clears his throat, tightens his paisley tie, and extends his arm, "You got a deal. We are good to go."

We shake hands. "Thank you and I'm glad we could make that happen. You have no idea how much you guys have come through for me today. This is my second car here and I won't go anywhere else."

The negative has changed into a positive. My spirits have been lifted. I ended up winning here in every way. Going from a 2017 to a 2019 model, from a car with 125,000 miles to a car with five. I have a smile from ear to ear when I see my payment is $450. I was paying $480.

Part II: Lessons

After leaving the dealership I head straight to work that night, grateful to turn on the rideshare apps. "Mmm…Aaah," smelling the wonderful brand new leather, "BILILING, BILILING, BILILING," my first ride in six weeks. It's at Rachels of Palm Beach strip club. I roll up and "B.I.G" Big Poppa is jamming through my new speakers.

I hop out under the awning where there are three strippers outside waiting and I open the door.

"Lexus?"

"Yes, that's us."

"Mayi?"

"Yes ma'am."

They squeeze in the back and Big Poppa is still jamming. "THUMP," I close the door and hustle back in. "We are going to Roccos Tacos in Boca Raton?"

"Yes! It's Taco Tuesday and we live down there."

"Great city. I grew up there. Nice place to be." I pull out of Rachels. "Ladies is the temperature O.K?"

"Yes. Thank you." Rachels is right next to the I-95 on ramp.

"Ladies you comfortable with seventy-five on the highway?"

"Go as fast as you want hun. Just get us there in one piece. Hey, it smells really good in here."

"Not to worry. I got you. It better smell good because I literally just got off the lot and picked you guys up. You're the first ones in my brand-new car."

"Nice! What is it? An Accord?"

"No. It's a 2019 Civic. They did a great job with this car."

"Yeah, they did. It's really nice."

"Thank you. So how long you guys been in Boca?"

"Just a few years. We go to F.A.U. What about you?"

"I grew up down there right behind F.A.U. I'll never forget my old address. Grew up there all my life. I live in Lake Worth now but I'm making my way back down there. That's for sure."

"Mayi. It was Mayi right?"

"Yes."

"This is Louann and Megan. I'm actually Alexus."

"Nice meeting you ladies."

"Nice meeting you. Mayi when we get closer, we are going to change. Is that O.K?"

"Absolutely. I don't see why not."

The ladies start talking amongst each other and I turn up the radio to DJ Khaled, "I'm the One."

Merging off on Glades Road one of the girls in the back says to the others, "Come on guys. We are almost there. Let's change." Seconds later, "Oh my! Look at her breast. Oh, my they are so nice and perky. Those are real? Look Megan."

"Look Mayi! Aren't they nice?"

How can I not look? I turn and take a peek before hopping onto Glades Road and stop at the light. Megan is fondling Louann, Louann is fondling Alexus, Alexus is fondling Megan and giggling. "Heheh. Nice. Heheh."

I'm really enjoying this and at the same time running through my head is, *"God help me! What is going on?"* Now I really don't know what I meant asking God to help me. All that came out of my mouth was, "Very nice ladies. You are very beautiful."

"Want to touch one?"

Oh boy! The light turns green. "I'd love to, but I have to drive. I'm flattered. You guys are crazy." A laugh comes out. I'm still grinning staring straight ahead in disbelief.

"Not crazy. Just fun." They finish changing and Alexus opines as we pull in. "Hey thanks for not forcing conversation on us. Some guys just don't shut up and keep trying to make conversation. It's so annoying. Hey, you sure you don't want to come hang out? We think you're pretty cool and cute."

"It's very tempting. You ladies are so pretty, but I just started working and I'm also still married. Going through a divorce, but I'm still married." I get out and open and close their door, "THUMP!"

"Well, if you finish early, come join us."

"I'll keep that in mind." The temptation is great. My need to work and get back on my feet is greater.

Her words remind me of lessons learned over time from driving. Lesson one is never force conversation on a passenger. Lesson two is, the more attractive the passenger, the less I start conversation. Engage in light conversation, but mainly keep it to the same basic questions. You don't want to be that annoying driver who doesn't leave a pretty lady alone.

Pulling over and waiting for my next call I dial Ricky Smalls. "Yo Rick I just had one of the craziest rides. Three strippers basically getting naked in the back."

"No way bro! You serious? Were they hot?"

"Picked them up at Rachels. What do you think?"

"Banging huh? You workin' late tonight?"

"Yeah man. Just got the new car today. Gonna be out late."

"I'll be here until Thursday. Then heading back down to Miami. Hit me up or come by."

"Got it. Later."

"Later."

Next call comes in and I'm on my way to pick up Bob. He's not too far at Town Center Mall. A text comes in, *"-Please pick up at food court-"* Arriving at the food court, Bob, his wife and two kids are outside waiting. They recognize my car from the app and approach. Bob sits up front with me, "Bob?"

"Yes. That's us."

"1311 12th St., Boynton Beach?"

"Yes sir."

Thirty seconds into the ride I can feel Bob's eyes fixated on me and as I'm approaching the green light, Bob asks, "Are you O.K to drive?"

"Bob what do you mean am I O.K. to drive? Am I driving bad?"

"You don't have diabetes or history of seizures or anything?"

"No Bob I don't. I'm curious. Why do you ask?"

"Mayi our first ride ever was horrific. Lucky for us it was all of us in that first ride. Long story short our driver had a seizure in the middle of the ride and because it was all of us, I had to sit in the front. Had it not been all of us we would have been in the back and God only knows. I had to lean over and take over the steering wheel while this guy was having a seizure. I maneuvered myself into the driver seat so I could control the pedals. Oh my God, it was awful."

"Bob that's crazy! I can't imagine. That's nuts! You don't have to worry about that here. No seizures or anything at all."

"Thank God. Not sure I could go through that again. The craziest part is when we got to my house and the ambulance arrives. Remember that dear?" He turns and looks at his wife.

"Oh, my that was crazy." She replies.

He continues, "They bring him back and he's having a panic attack with the paramedics and cop. Raging for them to get off him he punched the officer and ended up getting arrested."

I chime in. "What a night. He went out to make money and ended up getting arrested. That sucks."

"Your car smells nice. Is it new?"

"Actually, I bought it a few hours ago. You're my second ride in it."

"Mayi this is telling you to get off at Woolbright Road. Don't listen to it. Get off at the next exit, Boynton Beach Blvd. It will be a lot easier."

"No worries. Will do."

Bob points out, "Make a right here."

"O.K."

"Hey, Trumps doing a great job isn't he?"

"Yes, he is. He's doing awesome. I love him."

"Make a left here and then another left."

"Got it!"

I pull up to the driveway and Bob says, "Thanks for a smooth ride Mayi. A lot better than my first ride, that's for sure. You take great direction. You have a great night."

Lesson three is to learn to take direction. Don't be the guy who says, "GPS. I have to stick to the GPS," or the one who says, "Don't tell me how to drive. I know where I'm going." Um, no you don't have to stick to the GPS. You can take any route you want. Listen to the customer and take whatever route they want. They have probably done the ride so many more times than you.

"Thank you. You guys have a good night as well."

Before I even pull out of the driveway my next call comes in and a text with it. *"-Will be out at 10.-"* Lona is not out yet so I park in Duffy's parking spot and get out to wait by the passenger rear door. When Lona gets off at 10 P.M. and walks toward my car I confirm, "Lona?" and open the door.

"Yes, that's me." She ducks in and I close the door, "THUMP!" When I get in, I hear the comment I hear way too often from women. "Wow! That was nice. I don't remember the last time someone opened the door for me. It has to be at least five years."

"Come on! A pretty woman like you. Guys must be opening the doors for you. Let me confirm, 3343 Boynton Beach Blvd?"

"Yes, It's not that far. No. They don't but it's nice to know chivalry is not dead."

"Thanks. I don't know what's happening with my species. The least a man can do is open the door for a lady."

"I just watched a clip-on Trump while on break today. I can't stand him. He sucks."

"Yeah, I agree. The man does not know what he's doing. I'm glad I didn't vote for him."

Lesson four is to always agree whether it is your shared view or not. This is not the time to get ballsy. You always agree for the sake of a good smooth ride and a five-star rating. There is never ever any reason to be in any argument or confrontation with anyone in your car, EVER!

"This a new car? It smells new."

"Yes, I just bought it. You're my third ride in it."

"Awesome! I'm honored. It's really nice."

"Thank you. I love it."

"I like you. You single?"

"I wish. I'm getting a divorce."

"Well, that's like being single isn't it?"

I chuckle, "I guess so. I'm not sure."

"You got a great smile, too. How old are you?"

I still can't stop smiling, "Thank you. I'm forty-two."

"No way. You're forty-two? I thought you were like thirty or something."

"Thanks. I know right after my haircut and shave I look very young. I got a great bloodline. It runs in the family." She cracks a smile.

This is a pretty short ride and I arrive to Lona's townhouse.

"Hey, you're going to be driving tonight?"

"Yes ma'am. I am."

"Want a bump?"

"You know what? It's been a hell of a night and a hell of a few weeks and I just bought the car. I'm going to have to pass."

"Sniff…Sniff!" She takes two bumps.

I take off my seat belt, "Give me a minute, let me get that door."

"Aww. You don't have to do that. I got it."

"No, it's cool. We both win. It's part of my service and it gives me a chance to stretch my legs. Remember I'm in here a lot." She stands up and whispers, "You sure you don't want to come up and hang out with me?"

"I'm sure that I do but I can't mama. I just started working and have a little more tonight. I'm not sure I'm even ready."

"Awe. You're really sweet. You have a good night."

"Thank you, mama. You have a great night."

Lesson five goes to every damn man out there. OPEN HER DOOR! Open your woman's door. Open your friend's door. Open your mom's door. Open your sister's door. Don't let a woman open her door. That little gesture fellas will make a whole difference. Trust me on this.

I was going to end my night, but a call came into the queue before I even dropped Lona off. I turn on, "last call," on the app. I want to get home somewhat early so I can wake up at 5 A.M. and get back to it. I shake and bake like my stripper days and turn the corner into the hood in Boynton Beach on Martin Luther King Jr. Blvd. and see Slim at the pick-up location. Even in the hood, I open the door and confirm, "Slim?"

He looks at me like I have three heads. "Yes sir. That's me," and plops in. I close the door, "THUMP!"

I put the gear in "D" and take off. "3404 Swinton Road, Delray Beach?"

"Yeah, my G. Yo, you a crazy white boy hopping out like that. People get jacked around here."

"I can't go around living life scared, you feel me. I am Cuban."

"Aaahhhh...Cubano... Dale Papi. Let me ask you a question my G. You think if I throw you an extra five or ten we can make a quick stop at the corner store? I didn't know how to add the extra stop homes."

"No worries bro. You don't have to pay me for the stop. It's cool. I got you."

"You sure bro? I know it's extra time and distance."

"Slim I get paid for every minute and mile you're in my car. Now please keep it under five minutes because we only get paid fourteen cents per minute."

"Yo, my G. You're a pretty cool driver homes. I'm giving you a five star for sure."

"I appreciate that. That store right there on the corner?"

"Yeah homes. That's the one."

Slim runs into the corner store. My head is on a swivel. Whenever I drive at night, I'm on a swivel. Slim comes back, sits in the back and hands me a $5 bill. "My G. I really appreciate it. There are so many drivers that are assholes that wouldn't make the stop. You feel me homes? Take the five."

"Slim you didn't have to but it's much appreciated."

"No homes. Thank you. Appreciate you."

We leave the corner store and are about to hop on I-95 south on Boynton Beach Blvd. "Temperature O.K.?"

"Yeah homes, we good."

"You're comfortable with seventy five on the highway?"

"Yeah G. Yo my G, play that shit up loud. That some good Wiz Khalifa right there."

I oblige, cranking the dial almost to its max and merge onto the highway. Slim gets hyped in the back singing every lyric to "Black and Yellow." Slim jams out to the next song too, "Highest in the Room" by Travis Scott and by this time I'm on Atlantic making a left onto Swinton Road in Delray Beach.

"Yo, Slim we are here." I turn down the music.

"Yo my G, take this other five man. Great ride and music bro. Thanks for taking me to get my liquor."

"You're welcome. Appreciate that ten. Let me get that door for you."

"Nah G. U ain't gotta do that."

"I got you bro. I get to stretch out my legs anyways." I circle to the back of the car and open the door.

Slim stands up and says, "You still crazy you know that?"

I stick out my fist for a fist pound, "I've heard that before. You have a nice night brother."

He reciprocates the pound, "You to G. Be easy." I close his door, "THUMP," and rush into my car. I can get home in time to get six hours of sleep and be back out at 5 A.M.

Lesson six is to do the extra stop. Do not extort your customer. I'm sure that's why I'm always offered the extra cash. Don't give the customer a hard time. By not making the extra stop you're essentially taking money out of your own pocket. You're getting paid per time and distance they are in your car. I will initially let the customer know it's O.K. and that they don't have to do that. If they insist, I will take it. It's more awkward to keep rejecting it.

Lesson seven is the simplest lesson to follow yet many drivers don't do it. Keep your car clean inside and outside. People are paying for their ride. They want a nice clean sanitized ride. Make it smooth and clean and watch your tips go up.

My car does not carry candy, water or snacks. I was raised not to take anything from strangers. Most people understand that. I can't believe some people take these things. All an ill intention person would have to do is take a syringe and inject whatever substance into the item before you entered their car. Now you're done. Educate yourself and watch more I.D. channel like I did during my divorce depression. "Dateline" was my best friend.

Everyone is asleep in Malco's home. Tip toeing into the foreign room and turning the TV on low volume, the whispers of ESPN news lull me off to sleep.

5 A.M. arrives and I'm determined not to let myself fall back into a rut and have a productive week. That starts with attending church tonight. Instead of just attending Sundays I'm adding Wednesdays.

By 10:30 A.M. ride demand slows down giving me time to complete the paperwork to resolve the claim on the totaled Civic. Driving around running errands, I call PJ, my best man from my wedding. I have known him since we were nineteen. The phone rings two times. "Hello?

"Yo PJ! It's Mayi. How's it going up in shit town?"

"Bro, you know it sucks. It's cold here in Jersey. I can't wait to get back there. How are things with you man? With the wife?"

"Funny you said that. Bro I'm calling because I need a favor. You have any rooms at the Floridian on 6th and Congress?"

"Uh oh. What happened man? I thought you guys were working it out."

"Yeah bro, we tried. We constantly fight. It's just not working."

"You know I got you. I have a few apartments that are available. Go talk to Umberto. He takes care of everything there. I'll let him know you're coming. You guys will click. He's Cuban. You can move in this week for the rest of October if you want and we can just start everything in November. I can do $900 a month and it includes water. Don't worry about first, last or deposit."

"Bet. I owe you. Good looking out bro. I'm going to see him today. I'm moving in this weekend."

"Sounds good man. I'll see you when I come down next month."

"Cool bro. See you then."

"Late."

"Late."

I hang up and speed to the Floridian. Strolling into the office there is a man with an old school 70's porn mustache and beat up work jeans. His black shirt is untucked, and a Marlins cap sits on his head. His feet are up on the desk and he says, "You must be Mayi. PJ told me all about you."

"All lies. You must be Umberto." We both smile.

Umberto stands up and sticks his hand out. Looking up at him and extending my hand to shake his, he says, "Mayi I need you to fill out this application and everything else is already taken care of."

"No worries. Let me see that." I grab the black ball point pen and start filling out the application. Giving it a once over and handing it back to Umberto, "Here you go."

Umberto reviews quickly, and hands me the keys, "Welcome to the Floridian!"

"Thank you, sir. I'll be moving in this weekend."

"Move in whenever you want."

"Thank you." Rushing out into my car and feeling fortunate, "Hard Knock Life" by Jay-Z, plays in the background and my fingers tap to the beat on the steering wheel. Yelling to the heavens, "HECK YEAH! YES!"

My workday ends at 5 P.M and I make it to Malco's in time to change clothes for church. Malco and his wife are in his kitchen talking. Rushing into my room I grab black jeans and a green Abercrombie two button short sleeve shirt out of the closet. Shower, quickly shave, dry and throw on my outfit. My "Monkey Glue" yellow gel runs through my course hair and in between my fingers. It's spiked and thick. Smiling at myself in the mirror for the first time in a long time, I head out to greet Malco and his wife in the kitchen.

" Oye, le quiro dar las gracias por todo. I'm going to move out this weekend. Bro, PJ has a room and you're here with your family. I don't want to interfere. Pero le doy las gracias por todo!"

"Mayi tu saves que no hay poblema."

"Yo se bro. Heading to church. Talk to you later. Love you."

Skipping through his rocky driveway, I make it to my car and sit down to give thanks. "Dear Lord, thank you for what you have given me and what you haven't. Thank you for everyone you have brought in my life and everyone you have removed. I pray in the name of Jesus Christ that you forgive me for my earthly sins. Lord I don't just want to come to you when things are bad. Things have gotten on a roll and I know you are behind it. I thank you. Please open my heart for today's lesson. In the name of Jesus Christ I pray, Amen!" Slapping my shades over my eyes and pushing "Start," my car maps its way toward church.

Edward and Conny are greeting members at the entrance. There's no way to sneak past them. Not that I need to "sneak in" but I was still not up for socializing. I give them both a hug and kiss and they ask me to sit with them.

"How are you? How you holding up?"

"I'm doing pretty good. Ed, you know you're one of my rocks, right? That's why I come to you with all my questions. What you say always make so much sense after you make me research it."

"Thanks, Mayi. We love you."

Conny says, "We are here for you and whatever you need."

"You're the best Conny."

"You know you can come to our house anytime."

"I know. Thank you. Expect me some time soon."

Ed knows I sit quietly in the back row of church. "Mayi, you know you're going to have to sit in the front left with us and not in the back."

"Yup."

The band is playing "I Give You My Heart." We walk past the semi empty rows to the front left where Edward and Conny normally sit. We worship to a few other songs until the big screen rolls down. Edward and Conny are to my right. All are excited to see Pastor DS on screen and we take a seat. This man is blessed with effectively knowing how to deliver a message in a genuine and kind way. While he may not be aware of this, listening to him had a lot to do with my life changing and being saved. I have never returned to a church except this one. Edward and Conny are inspirational. I strive to be like Edward. This man loves Jesus and is so humble and full of humility. We connected right away being ex-athletes. I always tease him about being a southpaw.

Pastor DS is delivering a strong lesson. "Be ambassadors of Jesus Christ. How you might ask. Well, ask yourself, how are you living your life Christian? Are you being merciful and graceful? Are you being that light, that hope? Don't be intoxicated by the world. Be sober. Pray to Him. Talk to Him. Open the word. How many of you have a dog?" He pauses a brief moment. "Come on guys. This is not a trick question. How many of you have a dog?" Hands fly up in the air. "Much better. Now imagine waking up and there's that doggy sitting around waiting. Waiting for you to pet him or talk to him. That dog loves you so much that he's there waiting for you at the end of the day to get home no matter what kind of day you had. You open the door and there's the doggy again waiting, excited, no track of time. Panting and with his tongue out waiting for you to feed him, walk him, hug him, pet him and talk to him. Now replace that dog with Jesus. Remember dog spelled backwards is God. When you wake up Christian, He is there. He's there waiting for you to say hi. To talk to Him and have a relationship with Him. At the end of the day Christian He is there, no matter what kind of day. Waiting for you again to talk to Him. His love, grace and mercy will always be there. All you have to do is accept it. He is waiting for you to give it all to Him."

I look around and think, *"Don't cry. Whatever you do, don't cry. Don't cry here. Hold it together."* Choking up but trying my best not to cry, the tears come anyway. Pastor DS said a few other words, but none were as powerful to me as this.

After the message we worship to another song and I turn to Edward and Conny, "Guys, love you. Gotta run."

In order to move out that weekend, I am forced to pull out more Bitcoin to buy furniture for my little apartment. Days are spent talking to God, in the morning, in between rides, and at the end of the day, about everything and everyone. Sometimes asking Him to help me handle things better and sometimes asking Him to help others. I'm going to church two times a week and feel closer to Him.

Then, Saturday November 9th, happens. It was only a few weeks after purchasing my car. This is the first time I have told the truth about this story except to four people; the Officer I had to involve, PJ, Malco, and Ricky Smalls. They all laugh about it to this day, but the story brings shame on me. It's no one's fault, but mine. I gave in to the sin of lust.

The night started off with me catching up with some old friends at Old Key Lime in Lake Worth drinking beers and watching the boats go by on the intercoastal. Before COVID-19 this was my hang out. I felt comfortable within the lime green walls or when sitting outside at the tiki bar on the wicker chairs.

Thirty minutes in, I sit up and play ring toss behind the bar after ordering my $2 Yuengling. I'm playing ring toss, killing it, when a brunette in tight black shorts, a little sleeveless flowery top and a ball cap to the side, approaches and says, "You're pretty good. Want to show me how to play?"

I look over. "Sure. What's your name? I'm Mayi."

"Mayi I'm Jessica." She extends her arm.

We shake hands. "Nice to meet you. Jessica this game is a game of angles. If you stand here to the left of the hook, you have to throw the ring to the right, so it circles around like this." I stand to the left and throw the ring and it clamps on.

She smiles, "Nice."

I smile back, grab the ring, and reset. "Now, if you stand here to the right of the hook, you do the opposite and throw it to the left to circle the other way." I throw the ring, "PING," it ricochets off the hook, but you can see the main objective.

"Let me try." She giggles.

"Sure. Would you like a drink?"

"I'll take a Long Island. Thank you."

I stride my way to the bar. "Oye Pablo, make me a Long Island and another Yuengling for me."

"Got you Mayi."

Receiving the drinks and setting them on the tabletop next to the ring toss, we continue our night. Drinks keep flowing and we play ring toss into Sunday morning. I don't remember the rest of the conversation. She sneaks up behind me and wraps her arms around me, "Let's get out of here. I don't want to go home. You want to hang out?"

"Want to come over? I got my own place not too far from here." I turn and face her.

"Sure. I'll ride with you." She pecks my lips, takes my hand and leads me out. We are riding to my apartment and she says, "Nice car. Smells new."

"It is. Thanks."

We arrive at my apartment and sit on my grey "L" shaped couch, "You smoke weed?"

She puts her hand on my leg, "Yes I do. I'd love some." I get up and grab some weed and roll up a blunt. We talk for a minute while we smoke and watch Netflix. She takes a puff, lunges off the couch, and smushes her lips against mine. We start fooling around. She removes her top and rips off my shirt.

She lets me take off her shorts and I ask, "Should I get a condom?" Simple question. Get one means yes, don't get one means no, because I'm not having unprotected sex.

She moans, "Yes!"

Afterwards, I doze off for thirty minutes. Thirty minutes is all it took. I wake up and she's gone. Something felt off. I look outside and scream, "OH NO! My fucking car is gone! What the fuck?" I go around back. Nope. No car. I look around inside and also notice my monogrammed blanket with my last name stitched on it is gone. I'm running around my apartment like a mad man checking for everything: laptop, television, PS4, watch. She could have stolen these items as well but luckily; they were all in place. However, she did steal my car.

"Shit! Damn it! I'm so stupid!" I yell. I grab my phone and quickly dial 911.

"Hello 911. What's your emergency?"

"Yes, I have to report a theft. My car was stolen."

"O.K sir, what's your address so I can dispatch a unit to you?"

"3310 S. Congress Ave, Lake Worth, Apt. A."

"Sir, sit tight. A unit will be there in three minutes."

"O.K. Thank you." The call disconnects.

Pacing back and forth waiting for the officers, I contemplate my next move. *"What am I going to do. I can't believe this. What a couple months I'm having. Moved out, getting a divorce and totaled my money maker. This one gets stolen. I'm making some bad decisions. No one else to blame to Mayi."*

"Knock, knock," my thoughts are interrupted upon answering the door.

"Hi. You Mayi?"

"Yes sir."

"Mayi I'm officer Reyes. I heard there was a theft. Tu prefieres hablar Engles o Espanol?"

"Sabes, for the report let's do English. I can probably express myself in this circumstance better."

"O.K. Mayi shoot. Tell me what happened."

"Uhhhh…Man…I don't know how to tell you this. It's kinda embarrassing. I don't even know where to start." I'm looking Officer Reyes in the eyes.

"Look man you're not the first that this has happened to. You brought a girl home, didn't you? And she stole your car?"

The chair squeaks absorbing my weight and stress. "Yes sir. It's so embarrassing. I'm so stupid. I can't believe I let this happen in a moment of weakness."

With his eyes full of compassion, "Mayi, I'm going to help you. Look at the bright side. It didn't happen in front of any family so there's nothing to be embarrassed about there. Believe me this happens more often than you think."

I run my fingers through my hair. "O.K. officer Reyes. I just can't believe I let myself slip up like that."

"Hey it's O.K. It happens. The bad news is when we find these cars, if we find them, they are usually stripped down. You will be lucky to get that car back, luckier if in good shape."

"Just what I need. I rideshare full time. I just bought this car and had the one before it totaled. I guess I don't have any choice but to sit tight." I finish filling out the report and hand it to officer Reyes.

"I'm going to get out of here so I can enter this information into the data base. As soon as we know something, we will contact you." Officer Reyes stands up and we shake hands.

"Thank you, Officer." After closing the door, my feet are at it again and I feel like a fish circling the bowl. *"Who knows when or if this car will be found? I'm out of commission again."*

Feeling like the walls are caving in, I call Ricky to pick me up, hoping he won't ask too many questions.

Answering the door Ricky barges in, "Bro where is your car? I thought you just got a new one. You fuck that one up too?"

I look down and sigh, "Man you're not going to believe this. I finally brought a chick home, and she stole my car."

We leave my apartment and spend the ride down to Boca puffing, passing and laughing at my poor choices. We arrive at Ricky's bachelor pad on the 4th floor in the heart of downtown.

"Come. Let's go in the bathroom." I follow Ricky into the gorgeous golden Travertine and Saturnia 18x18 marble bathroom. He sits on his toilet lid and I sit on the jacuzzi ledge.

"You have had a heck of a month. Here hit this." Ricky extends his arm with a joint in his hand.

"Thanks bro. I could use that."

"That's crazy Mayi. I can't believe she did that bro. That's sick!"

I puff and pass. "Man I was just thinking how lucky I am. I had my Dad's 3K in the glove box. Could you imagine if I would have left his money in the car? I'm lucky I took it out last night or I would be down another 3K."

"Whoa! Bro you are so lucky!"

"I know. It's just a car. I got lucky. Something told me to take the money out last night. No reason to be out with it. She would have 3K on top of it." I can't help but crack a smile. I rub my hands over my face, "I'm so lucky!"

As if my day couldn't get any worse, "RING, RING, RING!" "Hola Papi. How are you?"

"Oye Mayi I'm O.K. I wanted to be the one to tell you. Mom and I are splitting up."

"Whaaaat?"

"You heard me. It's just not working."

"Papi after forty-five years at ages sixty-nine and sixty-five it's not working? You guys are really splitting up?"

"Si. We deserve to be happy and we are not."

"O.K. Papi. Me robaron el carro! Let me finish here and we can talk later."

"Que que?"

"Papi te llamo later and explain. I have to go. Love you!"

"Love you, Mayi."

Hanging up the phone, Ricky and I walk out from the bathroom to the balcony and sit on his two beige patio couches. He lights up a bitter smelling cancer stick, Marlboro 100's. He exhales, throws himself back and his arms over his head, "What are you going to do? Dude your parents."

Leaning back and looking into the horizon for answers, "I don't know. I have no clue. Not much I can do. I already reported the car stolen. So, it's just a waiting game. I have no idea what my parents are thinking."

"What did you tell the cop?"

"Bro I told him the truth. He was pretty cool. He was doing his best to make me feel comfortable. I wasn't going to lie to him. The cameras in my apartment complex caught everything and the property manager already saw it and showed it to the cop."

"Wow!"

"Bro he even said he saw me walk out like thirteen minutes after she left. Just fucking missed her. This is what I get man. Karma for all our stupid shit when we were kids."

Ricky finishes his cancer stick and stands up. "I'm going to get a head start on dinner." He slides the glass door shut and strolls into the kitchen. I stay outside wondering what my next move will be but the only thing that makes sense is to pray.

"Dear Lord, God thank you for everything you have given me and everything you haven't. Thank you for everyone you have brought in my life and everyone you have removed. Lord I am sorry for last night. I fell to my sin and I ask in the name of Jesus Christ for forgiveness. Lord, please find a way for me to get my car back. I'm really trying here. Please just give me my car back. I beg you please find a way. No matter what happens I will not give up on you. Please don't give up on me. Help me with my lustful heart. I can't do it alone. In the name of Jesus Christ I pray, Amen!"

Ricky comes to the glass door and slides it open. "Yo come in. The 1 o'clock games are about to start. Who do you like today?"

As I stand up and walk in, I say, "Man I haven't even looked. Ugh, I can't believe this bro. This shit sucks!" I walk inside, slouch on the white couch and fixate my eyes on the game. Ricky can cook and in-between games we eat.

"Yo this salad and teriyaki chicken is the bomb. How long you been marinating it?"

"Mayi for two days bro."

"Succulent as usual my friend. This thing is falling off the bone it's so tender and juicy."

Ricky licks his fingers. "I know bro."

After eating Ricky says, "Come on. Follow me." We go back to the bathroom and he rolls up two more joints.

"Mayi, you can stay here tonight if you want and I'll take you back tomorrow."

"Thank you, bro. I think I'll do that. I don't feel like being home tonight. Rick my parents are splitting up. My sister and I aren't talking. My wife ruined the relationship I took three years to repair with my sons' mom. I already know these holidays are going to suck. I think I'm going to take little man on a trip to Oklahoma. We could use the time away." We are puffing away. The smoke is evaporating into the air.

"That might be a good idea. Get away for a while. Look, I know you may be a little lonely right now with the split, but you can't be doing risky things bro. It could have been worse."

"I know bro. I have thought of that." Rick gets up and walks back out to the balcony to enjoy his tobacco. I walk into the living room and grab my laptop. Watching the second round of games I dial my cousin Los in Oklahoma.

In the biggest country accent, "Heeylo"

"Yo Los, It's Mayi. How's it going?"

"Deewd, a little cowld. How ya'll doin'?"

"Not bad bro. Mira, I want to come up with little man for Thanksgiving. What you think? That's cool?"

"Come on daawg. Be ready to be a man up hurr. Looking forward to seeing you and little man."

"Awesome bro. I'll let you go. Gonna' buy the tickets. See you soon. Love you."

"See you soon. Love you."

I hop on my laptop and find round trip tickets for $300 set to arrive November 25th at 9:30 A.M. and return Monday December 2nd at 10 P.M. I pump my fist, "YES!" Rick slides the glass door open and walks in.

"What's going on?"

"Bro I found round trip tickets to Oklahoma for $300 from the 25th until the 2nd."

"That's a great price!" Rick sits and we continue to watch the 4 o'clock games.

"I know man. I'm super excited. We could use the break."

The second round of football games come to an end and Rick and I are listening to the broadcasters when, "RING, RING, RING!" I don't recognize the number but it's probably a good idea to pick it up.

"Hello?"

"Yes, is this Mayi?"

"Yes, it is. Who's this?"

"Mayi this is officer Reyes. I spoke with you this morning."

"Yes, officer Reyes. How are you? How can I help you?"

"Mayi you're one lucky son of a gun. I'm happy to let you know that we have recovered your car. It's at Jupiter pound. You can call them and make arrangements to pick it up."

I jump out of my seat using all the energy left in me showing more exuberance than I have had all week yelling, "Are you serious? Get out of here! You guys found my car! Where was it?" Rick looks at me, eyes opened and astonished. I start to pace back and forth, totally freaked out and thankful.

"Jupiter P.D. got a hit on your tag. They found it parked at a KFC on Indiantown Road. You're very lucky. We normally don't find cars, especially in one piece."

"Thank you, Officer Reyes. I appreciate it."

"You have a good day son." We hang up. Rick and I are staring and grinning.

"Mayi you are one lucky mofo. You should write a book."

"Rick I'm going to order a rideshare and go get my car right now. I am not waiting. Hey, can I still come back? I don't want to stay at my apartment tonight."

"Yeah. No problem. I'll be here."

I order my rideshare to the Jupiter impound. We didn't speak much. $170 later, the car was back in my possession. I was feeling great until opening the car door. "Oh my God. What a bunch of slobs," I yell. My whole car, front to back was used as an ashtray. As if you lit a fire and kept all the windows down. Ash everywhere. They stole my

I.D. and my bible. Blunt wraps everywhere. Paperwork all over the place. They hit something while driving and left a dent on the bumper. Despite it all, I am still feeling grateful. How many people get their stolen car back the same day and in pretty good shape all things considering? Tomorrow I'm going to have to clean it really well and get back to work. I can't let this get to me. I start driving back, all my windows open, smiling ear to ear, wind howling, and I pray.

"Dear God. You are funny. I don't know what you're doing here but man are you funny. Thank you so much for my car. You came through for me big time. Thank you for giving me my daily bread, no matter what that bread is that day. Today's bread was patience and not losing it when I could have. Thank you for that patience and grace. I'm trying to learn and will find the lesson in today. God, I ask you to forgive me for my earthly sins and I thank you so much for tonight. In the name of Jesus Christ I pray, Amen!"

I'm riding back to Rick's excited. No music. Excited about the trip to Oklahoma. I get back to Boca and hop on the elevator to the 4th floor. Once inside, he yells, "Yo! You got your car?"

"Yeah bro. Damn I'm exhausted," and slouch on the couch. Before the 8 P.M. game makes the fourth quarter I knock out. The next day is spent scrubbing and having the car detailed at the legendary Boca car wash on Glades Road and Federal Highway. I get to work, busting my butt every day until the day of the trip so I can have the Thanksgiving time off without bills on my mind. I pick up my son Sunday the 24th. He runs to the trunk to drop his bags and then opens the driver door to give me a hug and a kiss on the cheek.

"Hey bud! I missed you. You excited?"

"Yeah Papi. I can't wait to see everyone in Oklahoma."

"You have warm clothes, right? It's going to be cold!"

"Yes Papi!"

"O.K. Make sure everything is ready for tomorrow morning. Abuelo is taking us to the airport early."

"O.K."

We get home and fall asleep early. I don't care how big my 12-year-old may be. He will always be my baby, so I cuddle with him. He's my teddy bear. My father picks us up and on the way to the airport says, "You want to tell me what happened with your car?"

I look at my Pop with a shit grin, "Nope! We can talk about it when I get back. Not enough time and little man is here."

"O.K. Mayi. We do have to have a talk when you get back."

"Si Papi. Yo se! We really do!"

My Apartment

THE MAKING OF MAYI

Upon landing in Will Rogers World Airport, I call my oldest cousin. "Yo Los, where you at?"

"You need to walk to arrivals on the first floor. I'm here in the red truck out front of the terminal."

We make our way down and can't miss the Santa Claus white beard my cousin loves to sport shaped around his big-ass bright white country smile, "Howdy y'all! Welcome to Oklahoooma!" He gives my son a huge embrace.

"What's up little man? Man, you're almost bigger than your dad."

"Yeah, my dad is little. Where are the boys?"

These two are roasting me, but it's a welcome jab amongst family. We load the trunk with our luggage. "Yeehaw!" I yell, hopping into the front seat of his pick-up.

"You will see them tonight. One is hanging with his girlfriend and the other is home waiting for us. Just came from the office."

Los is Yez's older brother. He's what we call a Guajito. That's a Country-Cuban. I'm talking large-brimmed cowboy hat, straw in the mouth, big, buckled belt with western boots. Los is a Navy vet. He once almost threw a guy off his ship. The guy must have been an asshole looking for trouble becasue Los has a huge heart, but no room for bullshit.

We leave the airport and hit open road. It's a gorgeous day in Oklahoma. Very different from Florida. The wind reminds me of Chicago. It's not the temperature. It's the wind that accompanies it. Forty degrees, fifty MPH winds at the moment. Flat orange dirt. Dead dry bushes. Very rocky. Looks like orange baseball clay all around. Dead yellowed grass is the norm. We pass a several oil rigs and I ask, "How's Samantha? The boys? How did he do in baseball?"

"Samantha is great. Deewd, I'm blessed. Boys are great. He had a great baseball season. Couple schools are looking at him."

"Congrats. Agency doing well?"

"Better than ever. Everything is good Mayi." He points out in front of him. "Sometimes you will see deer out hurr."

"Can you hunt them?"

Los responds, "Only during hunting season Einstein." My kid laughs.

I look back. "What's so funny chump?"

He squirms, "Nothing Papi. You're getting roasted today." Kid gets a bigger smile.

Los looks in the rearview mirror. "What you laughing about brain. Your dad told me about your grades and school. You better wake up."

Los looks at me and snarks, "Look Mayi. He ain't smiling no more. Look, look pobresito."

"Hey what city do you live in again?"

"Yukon. It's about forty-five minutes away. We got twenty minutes left." Los throws on his country music. We hear a little Hank Williams and Kenny Rogers. We arrive at Los' cozy home. He has the house right at the crescent of the cul-de-sac. Prime time real estate. Old school brick home. Brown leaves all over the ground falling from the trees. They are swirling around non-stop. Big oak tree square in the middle of the front of the lot.

We grab our bags and rush out of the wind. Los wife, Samantha is in the kitchen.

"Hi Mayi! Hi little man. Great seeing you guys." We give each other hugs and kisses.

"Hi Sam. Great seeing you mama. Thank you, guys, for having us."

"Thank you, guys, for coming. It will make a nice Thanksgiving," she says.

My son runs straight into the room to play with his cousin.

"Mayi come hurr. Let's go to the backyard for a second." Los leads me to the backyard. There is a long pool covered with a tarp, so the leaves don't fall in, no matter how hard they try. Adjacent to the pool sits four wide jugs towering several feet, filled with water to the brim. "Mayi fill those white containers on those cages with the water from the jugs for the rabbits. I'll feed the chickens."

"Got it."

Los' home is like Noah's Ark. He has two dogs, one cat, sixteen chickens and twelve bunnies.

"You see that Mayi? All my animals gotta get along. You don't get along, you gotta go." We laugh through the chores.

"Mayi come hurr. Come hurr quick." He leads me into a private room in the house. "This is my war room." He waves his arms across packed shelves like he is introducing a beauty queen.

"Wow Los! You are hard core!"

"Mayi the shit hits the fan; I'm giving you twenty-four hours to get up hurr. After twenty-four hours, I don't know you. You might get shot."

"What the hell? No joke! How long does it take to drive up here from Florida?"

"Dog I did it nonstop in about twenty-two hours. Listen I'm giving you two extra hours bro." I smile. "So, let me show you around." Los starts at one end of the room, "Count them. Come on. Count them."

I'm going to spare you because my cousin is like a little kid at a candy store when it comes to showing off his stockpile. It is one impressive stockpile. If I really write the dialogue of how he had me count everything in that room, we will be here for hours. There were twenty-seven 5lb. buckets of rice, two hundred jars of beans, seven different fruits-one hundred jars of each. One hundred jars of every spice you can imagine, from oregano, pepper, turmeric, to parsley, cumin, and garlic. Fifty-gallon water jugs. At least twelve cases of water bottles lined a wall, twenty survival books sit on the wooden bookcase next to about a dozen guns. That's just in this room. In the house lies a gun in every room, including the bathrooms. Who the hell keeps guns in the bathroom? Don't go looking for trouble at that house because it will surely find you.

"Mayi let me finish showing you around." He finishes the tour in his master bath. "Come hurr, look." He shows me two more guns. One under the toilet and another under the sink. "Come on. Let's go check on the food. I left ribs in the grill on low heat this morning before I left." He redirects to the kitchen and grabs two Heinekens . "POP," "POP,"

We grab our bottles and continue to the grill in the backyard. He raises the lid. "Mmm...smells delicious!" I exclaim as Los flips the golden warm, caramel basted, crispy ribs around.

"Cheers!" Los says as he hits the lip of my bottle.

"Mayi guess how much I got this house for?"

"I know it's going to be lower because you said that but if I was taking a true guess I would say 230k to 250k."

He smirks, "143k."

"No way!"

"Yup."

"My townhouse cost $235k."

"Homes are cheap out here because of tornadoes."

"Ah, I see."

We drink a few more beers catching up on old times. The boy are busy playing virtual reality and the adults want to try.

"Come on. Old man going to show you young bucks how it's done. Let me see that boxing game." I say.

My fists virtually knock the computer generated boxer down in the first round. "UG, MMFF, AH, BAM!" I'm successful, but exhausted and out of shape. It slipped my mind that I just drank four beers.On round three my body falls straight to the ground. "Aahhhh. I'm so nauseas. Ahhh, this sucks."

"HAHAHA…HAHAHA!" The boys laugh as I crawl to the bathroom to hover my head over the toilet.

I throw up and of course, my smart ass cousin posts up against the bathroom door.

"Deeewd…Daawg…you just broke the record. The fastest anyone visiting has ever thrown up."

He yells at his wife. "Babe! Mayi broke a record already. Babe! Mayi's throwing up three hours off the plane."

Sam's laughter crosses two rooms. "Oh Mayi you ain't gonna make it around here like that!"

"Gee, thanks guys! It wasn't the beer. It was how hard I went right after drinking beer. This VR stuff is intense."

"Hey, I don't know daawg, I know what I saw." Still on my knees, I crawl to the door and slam it shut.

Throwing up always makes me feel better. I make it to the living room where Los is watching the weather channel. "Los I'm gonna lay down until dinner."

"Yeah. That's a good idea Cinderella Man."

A few hours later, the sound of kids running in the hallway awakens me. My grumbling stomach tells me its dinner time. We all sit down around the table and eat the bone tender ribs Los made with home-made black beans and rice. We talk a little baseball and Oklahoma weather.

"Mayi tomorrow you and little man put on some long sleeves and jeans. We are going sight-seeing around town."

"Sounds good. What time you want us up?"

"Be ready by 8:30 in the morning. We can get an early start."

"10-4. Sounds good."

Before dozing off my son hugs me. "Papi thank you for bringing me. This is the best trip ever."

"I'm glad you're having fun Papo. Let's hit the hay. We got a big day tomorrow. Love you! Goodnight."

"Goodnight Papi."

I get up at the crack of dawn. My body clock is still off by an hour. Los and I are the first up. After throwing on my black jeans with a hoody and a beanie to cover my head I nudge my son. "Hey bud, get up. Get ready. Come on. Let's go."

He pops up right away. "Papi, I'm ready. Just going to brush my teeth and eat cereal. I'll be ready in fifteen minutes."

Meeting Los in the backyard he hollers to me, "You know the drill. I got the chickens." My hand freezes up and my body shivers dipping my hands into the icy water jug.

"Little man is up and will be ready soon. He's in the kitchen eating cereal."

"O.K. when he's done, we are gone."

We finish with the animals in the back and rush back in. "BRRRR," I open my eyes wide and cross my arms. "Little man you ready to learn a little history today?"

"Yes zirrr!"

"Los let's roll."

"Let's go."

We run to the truck and set out through rural dusty roads to reach downtown. The dirt around us is mushy and muddy. I still can't get over how orange everything is. The cold weather and the country are a nice change. We pass yellow wheat farms and arrive at a ranch.

"Wow Papi! Look at all the cattle. My first time seeing these." My cousin and I look at each other with and smile.

"Papo those are longhorns." I educate him.

Los is wearing his cowboy boots with little sheriff stars. "Guys come hurr." We follow him into the barn. "These huge horses are Clydesdale's. You will notice these are twice the size of my beautiful black Arabian show horse over here." Los continues to the back of the barn and walks in to feed his horse.

"Wow Tio. You own a horse? That's so cool."

"Come on daaawg. You two go to the truck and clean your shoes. I'll be right there."

Los finishes feeding his horse and we get back on the road. We arrive at the Oklahoma City Memorial. Strolling with our heads low respecting the somber tone, we pass the pond in the middle of the memorial that leads to the big wall with names of the victims of the terrorist bombing. Big and small brown chairs symbolize the lives lost in a building. Los educates, "Little man there was a bombing here. Kids in a nursery and other federal workers were killed. This is the remaining site. You weren't even born yet son."

Little man looks confused, in disbelief. He tugs on my sweater and whispers "I can't believe people are like that."

"Bud, there are just some bad people out there." We finish walking the memorial and some of Oklahoma City. Our faces are red. My son's lips are purple. You can hear the piercing wind whistle. "WEEEERE…WEEEERE."

"Los these winds have to be at least fifty miles per hour. Let's go. That's enough for today."

We hustle back to the truck and head home. I can see the shock in my son's face. The blank expression and silence says it all. We arrive home to leaves swirling around us. My son and I bulldoze our way inside while my cousin takes his time. Sam is waiting at the table and smiles, "Hey guys. How was your day?"

Little man kisses her on the cheek. "It was a learning experience that's for sure."

"Nice. Where did you go? What did you do?"

"We went and saw longhorns and your horse. Oh! And we went downtown. That part was sad."

"He took you to the memorial huh?"

My son replies, "Yeah, boys in the room?"

"Yes." Sam points to the bedroom and he leaves to join them.

Los and I join Sam at the table, have a couple of beers and conversation about Thanksgiving and the weekend when I request, "I want to go to church Sunday."

"Deeewd...that's a given at my house."

We chit-chat a little longer until dinner time. Every night there, with the exception of one, we ate dinner together. We finished eating and got ready for bed. The next day we laid around and relaxed. We didn't do too much since Thanksgiving was around the corner.

Thanksgiving morning everyone ran around like chickens with their heads cut off, or maybe, more appropriately, turkeys. Running around to get ready, complete the traditional dishes, make holiday calls of well-wishes, and pack the car. We visited two houses that day. Sam's parents and her Grandma's. Awesome country people with a patient, kind way about them. Very welcoming.

Sam's dad approaches me. "I reckon you're Los's little cousin."

"Yes sir, that's right."

"I feel bad for you. You're related to that son bitch?"

I extend my hand, "You feel bad for me? Don't feel bad for me. I had to deal with him. He's your problem now."

He shakes my hand. "Los, I like this feller here. You damn Cubanos all funny." We laugh at each other. I have my son make the rounds with me and greet everyone in the room. We all interlock fingers in a big circle. Sam's mom shares a beautiful grace in her warm, soft voice.

"And all his people said-"

"Amen!"

We eat until our sides hurt from all the grub. Some are in the kitchen talking and laughing it up. Some are in the living room watching the Thanksgiving football game. After the first NFL game we prepare to leave. We are going to make our way to Sam's parents for her mom's dessert and the second game. If there is anyone who can make dessert as good as my mom, it was Sam's mother. The creamy rich pies filled the air with sugary-sweet aroma. She made an abundance of pies, at least eight. We ate and communed until the game was over. I was so stuffed you could have rolled me home. Luckily, they live around the corner.

After his tryptophan coma wore off he popped up from the recliner "Guys time to go."

"You boys go. I'm going to stay here a little longer," Sam replies.

"So are we. We want more pie," the kids replied.

"I'm coming with you. I'm exhausted myself," I say.

Los and I give the ladies a goodbye kiss. I put my arm around Sam's father's shoulder and whisper, "It's a shame what you Oklahoma fans have to go through. You might lose this week to State."

He looks at me wide-eyed, rolling a toothpick between his lips, smacks the back of my shoulder, peers at Los, and says, "Los you don't get to pick 'em do you? I really do like this feller here. You make sure you come back. Oh. Don't bring none of those U.M. thugs."

"That's a low blow." Los and I laugh our way out the door. We stroll back to his home, watching our breath blow cold air ahead of our footsteps. Once home, we make ourselves comfortable in the living room, falling asleep to the sound of the 8 o'clock game.

We spent the next two days towing the kids. We hit the local mall, downtown, and Oklahoma's minor league baseball stadium where we rode inner tubes down man-made snow slopes. We snapped my favorite picture of the trip huddling under a forty-foot Christmas tree with ornaments the size of softballs.

Our last day in Oklahoma comes quick. We wake up Sunday morning and my cousin and his wife fulfill my wish. We are headed to Discovery church in Yukon with her parents. Los and I take one car and Sam rides with her parents. We meet for service and they introduce me to the pastor who seems engaged with his congregation. This is one of those mega churches that airs live online, similar to my church back home. We worship a few songs. The pastor prays and begins his message.

"Brothers and sisters today I want to talk about hope. I know that during these festive times and holidays some get depressed. A lot of suicides happen during these times. You see it's not so festive for some. Some look for the answers at the bottom of a bottle, but you never do quite get to the bottom of that bottle or find the answer for that matter, do you? Some look for the answer in the form of a pill. Sometimes you do reach the bottom of that bottle for the last time. Some inhale their answer. But you never know when that might be your last breath. I want you to do something with me. Come on everyone now. Everyone take a deep breath."

"Aaahhh…Whooo," half gasped the crowd.

"Oh, come on now. We got a full congregation and that's all you can give me brothers and sisters?" Chuckles echo through the sanctuary. "Come on. Everyone with me. Take a deep breath on three. One, two, three!"

"AAAAHHHH…WHHOOOO!" The group roars until they run out of breath.

"Much better. You see, that was a miracle from God. You are here. You are alive. There is hope! I am hopeful. We have got to learn to move on and give it to God. Have faith. Have hope in Him. Give it to Him."

Uh oh! Here we go again. Something about church and Jesus that just chokes me up. Ever since I have seen the movie of Jesus Christ as an adult and fully grasped the meaning, I ask why? How? It chokes me up. I know Los sees me crying and peeks intermittently, but keeps trying to stare forward like he does not notice. Sam is next to me rubbing my shoulder and upper back. Her mom rubs my other shoulder. At the end of the service, they call for altar call and rededication. With my head low, I head to the altar for rededication. Sam and her mom creep up and stand next to me for support. We pray with the Pastor.

"God bless you brothers and sisters. May the Lord give you strength in your time of trouble and when you're weary. Lord guide my brother Mayi and lead him away from evil and temptation. Guide him with his next steps. In the name of Jesus, we pray."

"Amen!"

They both extend a warm embrace. Making my way to Los, I stop and turn as if I'm looking at someone in the crowd, taking a moment to wipe my eyes. Then, I continue over to everyone. The ladies are lost in gossip with their friends.

"Come on let's go. I already told the ladies we were leaving. They are meeting us back at the house." Los says.

"O.K., Let's go."

We make ourselves the complimentary coffee before we leave, not to drink, but to warm our hands. We enter the truck and buckle up. Los places his right arm atop my left arm, grabbing my hand over the center console and squeezes, "Brother I've been meaning to have this talk with you. You can call me a dick or whatever you want or not call me again at all, but I'm telling you this because I love you. Brother, I don't know what kind of parenting skills you have, but I saw a great father. You need to get back to Florida and fight for your kid." When the, "brother" term gets thrown around, I know Los means business.

"I can't. He doesn't want to leave his mother. He doesn't want to leave his little sister alone. I can't spend money on lawyers only to have him turn around and tell the judge he doesn't want to leave. I have had this talk with him numerous times. He's not ready."

"Have you talked to him lately? He's a great kid deewd. I would hate to see him be screeewed up."

"Me and you both."

"Brother, I have never seen such nice guys be such screw-ups. My brother, Jaxson, you! You guys are so nice, but you're so messed up. Goon used to be a screw-up, too, but he managed to find a good woman, and now he's not. He is the only one."

"Did you know Jaxson got married?" Los gives me a funny look.

"Whaaaat? No way!" He focuses back on the road and puts both hands firmly on the steering wheel.

"Yeah man. Who knew? No one did. Bro she reminds me exactly of his mom and sister. Real nice girl. He's doing well. He's been married for a minute now. He's trying man. Finally, after so many years, he's trying."

"Another thing, brother. Go home and fix things with your sister. You only have one. Get your divorce settled and your home in order."

"Not sure how my sister and I are gonna fix things. We haven't talked in over a year. We don't have much to say to each other. We don't see eye-to-eye. We think very differently. I don't go to my parents because it's so weird between us."

"I don't care how you fix it, fix it! How's your dad? You know, we heard about everything with your mom. Sorry, brother."

"How do you know about that?"

Los smirks, "Come on daaawg. You know I know everything before it even happens."

"I guess he's good all things cosidering. Whatever! They are splitting up. My wife is filing for divorce. Little man's mom sucks. Can't seem to keep her mouth or legs closed. He's heard her so many times in her room. I don't care what she does, but she needs to do it when she doesn't have custody of him."

"Deeewd stop smoking pot and get your shit together. You're too smart and nice to be going through this. Get away if you have to, but make sure whenever or wherever you go, that you're certain you're never returning. Never looking back. I love it hurrr!"

"Bro, you know I gave up ten years to run my parent's store. I had to sacrifice for them just like they did for me all those years. Made garbage-money, but I had to do it. Some things, like family, are more important than money. Trust me, I never thought this is where I would be in life right now." I look down and sigh.

Five minutes away from his house Los continues. "Mayi get your shit together and we need to break this generational curse for my kid's sake and for yours. You know our Grandma did Voodoo. No one in our family practices Christianity except my mom, you and me. No one else in our family has been saved. None of them really believe."

"I'm trying bro. I wish there was more I could do for little man. Life is hard but like the Pastor said, I'm still here man. I'm still standing. Hustling and bustling. You might knock me down seven times but I'm getting up eight." We arrive at Los's house; he grabs my arm again and looks right through me.

"Soooo, let me tell you the kicker."

"O.K., go for it."

"Now, I know you have heard rumors and have been asking around so I'm going to confirm it for you."

"Yeah man, what is it?"

"The rumors are true. Our grandfather in Cuba was a pimp and our grandmother was his madame."

"Wait! What! I always thought Yez and Jaxson were screwing with me!"

"That's the generational curse we need to break."

His statement sat with me from that moment all the way through the flight home. It floored me only because it made so much sense. Memories come flooding back to me. *"She practiced voodoo and was a madame? What does that mean to me? Which curse is he talking about? I saw that chicken sacrifice at six years old in her kitchen. Blood everywhere man. No wonder I was so scared of that damn house. Did that curse me?"*

When I get back to Florida my commitment to church deepens. I continue to work hard and keep my mind occupied. Next thing I know, its New Year's Eve 2019. I'm in my apartment, moping on my grey couch, wearing shiny tan Doc Martin dress shoes and black jeans. I've had a month to process all this life changing information. In the span of three months, I'm getting divorced. My parents are splitting up. Now, come to find out my grandpa was a real-life pimp, and my grandma was his madame in Cuba. This explains volumes about me and my family. The machismo and lust from top to bottom. The womanizing.

I'm watching TV waiting for the evening to come. A box of family pictures sits next to me. I glance down and come across a picture of my grandfather in the box. It triggers me to search for a video I have of him and my son together saved in my phone. My eyes squint and redden as I take a deep breath listening to my son play guitar with my grandpa in the background.

"Tuvo que hacer Mexicano cono!" My grandpa's voice is faintly heard.

"Ya tu sabes abuelo." I responded in the video.

Tears fall down my face. My grandfather passed in November 2017 at the age of ninety-six. Loved him. He was a great man from my experience. No pimp behavior I could spy. He loved his kids, grandkids, great grandkid, pretty much everyone. A simple man who loved to ride the Tri-Rail to Miami. He always had a smile on his face and taught us to do right. Ironic considering his previous "profession." From family stories growing up, in Cuba you did what you had to do to survive.

I began to wonder, *"Maybe my lust for women and female attention was inherited. Could that be why I stripped for three years in my twenties? Sure, I liked the money, but I enjoyed dancing and the reaction from the ladies. Was I the madame or the pimp?*

The scene of how I lost my virginity replays like a movie in my head.

"You sure about this?" I whispered as my lips pressed against hers.

"Yes. Uh huh. I'm ready." She scratched my back lighlty.

"You sure? We don't have to do this."

"No, I want to. I love you." She cooed in my ear.

"I love you too."

Boom! Two minutes later, just like that, we lost our virginity to each other. We didn't know anything about love. I sure didn't. We dated for three years. I cheated on her with over twenty girls easily. I apologized years later, and she accepted.

"Man, just get to church and stop this nonsense."

Dropping that picture outside the box, out falls an old polaroid. I had to be six years old, wearing big white socks up to my knees with brown stripes, white shorts, and a brown shirt. Even then, I had to match. It was a straight off the boat outfit, early 80's. I was sporting a mullet. You could always find me out on the street playing sports against the big kids on the block. My competitive spirit was strong. Many days we played "Murder Ball." We made the biggest ramps we could and jumped them on our bikes. I almost lost the eye falling into branches from a failed jump. Still have the scar to prove it.

I'm shuffling and ruffling around through the photos wasting time. The waterworks start running down my face, again. I flip over an old black and white picture that was sitting upside down. One corner is ripped off. The other corner is folded in dog-ear fashion. The borders are wrinkled, frayed and slit in a few areas. The picture is of my parents in happier days. It crushes me. I wish for simpler times, staring at the picture and thinking about the house my parents had in Boca Raton near the beach. Things were so easy back then. I'm astonished by how young my father is in this picture and how much we look alike.

My father is intelligent and a perfectionist. He remodeled his home by himself. He excels in math and works miracles with his hands, yet was only afforded a 5th grade education. The picture reflects the time period when he opened his first successful flooring business. Same time he signed me up for baseball at eight years old.

At first, I hated baseball. Not because I wasn't any good at it. I would beg, "Papi let's go bowling. Can we go bowling tonight? You said we would go bowling tonight."

"Mayi tomorrow. There's a baseball game tonight. It's the last game. We can go tomorrow."

"Ugg…O.K. Papi." The next night would come around. "Papi don't forget we are going bowling tonight."

"Mayi I'm sorry. This should be the last game. There is only one more."

This happened so many times. Little did I know he was watching playoff games and world series games that he thought would eliminate on those nights. It gave me a dislike for baseball.

My mother was doing what most immigrant women did at that time, clean houses for rich clients in Boca. She is meticulous, sweet and a hard worker. They worked their asses off to live the American dream and gave their children everything.

My anger and hurt enslave me. I take that picture and rip it up. Tossing it in the trash, more tears run down my face. A glutton for punishment, I see my baseball articles and report cards all bunched at the bottom of the box. My fingers pinch and slowly unfold the grey and yellow-stained article. It reads "Boca Raton's KILLER B's." We went 37-1 in our B competition and 6-5 against A teams, winning against Boca's A team. I was seventeen-years old playing teams loaded with college and pro players.

I ended up playing for twelve years, one season blending in to the next, with the exception of two years that I played football. Baseball grew to be my first love. I slept, drank, ate, and shit baseball, winning numerous accolades. Tournament MVP's, All-Tournament team, on and on, and on. I had the same coach for a six-year stint.

"Mayi we have won the city championship the last six years in a row."

"It's been six years together, huh? Good coaching.Thanks to you."

"With good players," Coach Mik would respond.

I pitched in a few games. Even played in a state championship game. We played against A-Rod, Rick Ankiel, and other future pros. Managed to travel all over the state thanks to baseball. The game relies on friendships and hard discipline. I recieved a full ride for baseball and grades at Northwood University in West Palm Beach.

My Super-Dad maybe missed five games my entire career. Unfortunately, I played in the 90's Steroid Era. Every player around me in college was on the program, but me. If locker room walls could talk, they would yell and scream while having loud 'roid rages. The fight between teammates Jacob and Roger still sticks with me.

"Hey, Roger, why don't you hustle more on the ground balls, so we don't have to run?" Jacob yells unnecessarily from a few feet away.

Roger has his back turned to Jacob and looks over his left shoulder. Attempting to walk away he yells back "Jacob kiss my ass!" This battle had been brewing the entire practice and Jacob took offense. His face turns crimson, he takes a deep breath, runs full force toward Roger and shoves him with all his might. Roger falls in fair territory on home plate, landing on his back and grabbing his neck. "Ah my neck, my neck. What the hell were you thinking? Fuck, owwww, my neck!" Jacob broke Roger's clavicle.

The article manages to give me a smile. I carefully fold it back up and place it back in the box. I vow to change my somber mood and keep perusing through photos.

A picture with five guys in bright shirts captures my attention. I take a deep, deep breath. I see my cousins, Goon, Los, Yez and Jaxson. "Oh boy" I utter. My eyes fixed on this picture.

My cousins are a mirror to my past and present, reflecting the good and bad behavior of my youth into adulthood. Sometimes I do not like the reflection. We attended the same schools and detentions at times. They called me "cry baby" because I was sensitive. Not an embraced quality as a Cuban man. I really like this picture of us and stick it on my fridge using my #1 Dad magnet.

At fifteen while focused on baseball, I still managed to find time to get in trouble. It's during this period that Jorge and I become best friends.

"Yo Mayi. I need help jacking a stereo system tonight," said Jorge.

"Bro how are we going to do that?"

"Mayi I know a car that's always bumping around here. We can go late at night."

"O.K but how are we going to break in?"

"Dude all we need to do is buy a couple of spark plugs and break the top porcelain off. The porcelain is denser than the glass. It will cause the glass to shatter when we throw it at the window."

"Bro you have done this before. You sure man?"

"Gone with my brother a couple of times. Come on dude. It will be fun."

"Screw it! Why not?"

"Cool! We will be straight. Just gotta cover each other's backs. First we are gonna get a pizza."

"We have no money. We can't order a pizza."

"You see that house across the pond?"

"Yeah."

"I'm gonna order them a pizza and when he delivers it, I'm gonna take one from the car."

"Bro you're crazy."

"Watch!"

This is the extent of my juvenile criminal career. Breaking the law wasn't really my thing. We never got caught. I lived a double life. I still said no to drugs because I was caught up in playing baseball. I was able to do whatever I wanted simply because I was an athlete, getting good grades, and not getting in trouble (at least as far as they knew.)

I could walk in and out the front door, waving goodbye to my parents, no questions asked, stroll back in, anytime, day or night.

"Ma, Pa, I'll be back at eleven. Going to work on a project."

"O.K. please lock the front door. Take your key in case we are sleeping."

I look up to my father, but it was hard growing up a perfectionist's son. My pops would always bust my balls about my grades.

"This B. No good. No good this B. I want A."

"O.K. dad. You know a B is good, too."

I found the only piece of sexual advice he ever gave me odd, but it stuck.

I was partnered up with a female dancer at my cousin's Quinciniera practice. The girl kept coming on to me. I was freshly into my first relationship and kept resisting. Naïve, horny, and fifteen, I caved. I felt so guilty. I had my dad drive me to my girlfriend's house that night to confess. We argued, we cried, we argued, we cried and then, finally made up.

My dad was watching from his black SUV. I gave her a good-bye kiss and climbed up into the passenger side. After pulling out of her driveway we pause at the stop sign and my father pivots in my direction. He stretches his arm behind my head rest and stares at me. I finally ask, "What's up? What's wrong?"

"If a girl wants to have sex with you, you protect yourself and you have sex with her. You hear me? I don't want to hear anything about you being un Maricone."

This is my Cuban culture. The machismo men. The stigma. And there you have it. The advice that I think has forever guided me and I run away from now, like I should have at fifteen. Live and learn.

"RING, RING, RING!" My phone rings me back to the present.

"Goon what's up bro? Happy New Year."

"What are you doing tonight?"

"You know I gotta drive. Tonight, is a big night."

"Why don't you stop by before you drive?"

I look at my watch. "It's four. I can probably swing it. I'm not feeling well man. Kinda going through some stuff. Why don't I come over now?"

"No shit Sherlock. I'm home with the girls. Get over."

"See ya!"

I hang up the phone and leave the boxes on the dining table. Heading out the door I grab my keys and wallet. Trying to remain upbeat I turn the music up playing "Side to Side," by Arianna Grande jamming to beats the whole way. While singing loudly to my own made-up lyrics as all people do, another call comes in.

"RING, RING, RING!" It's Yez. "Yo, Happy New year bro."

"Hey Mayi, what you doing tonight?"

"Bro I gotta work. Big night. I'm on my way to see Goon. I'll stop by after I see him before I go to work."

"Dale, I'll see you here."

"Dale, Later!"

I park and knock-on Goons door. "WOOF…WOOF…WOOF!" The familiar barks of their dogs Casper and Jasper answer on the other end. Casper is a ninety-pound puppy with a beautiful shiny coat and adoringly looks up to the smaller elder Jasper. Holding Jasper and Casper back Goon opens the door and ushers me in. Growing up we were the closest, being the same age, and living in thew same neighborghood. He's got me by three months and five inches.

"What's up Goon man? How you been? How's the wife? She at work?

"Yeah, Mayi she is. I'm good bro. Can't complain." Walking into the kitchen, his skinny jeans drag across the porcelain floor making a swishing sound. He opens the fridge and grabs two red cans. "Hey man, want a beer?"

"Yeah. I can have one or two."

"Come on. Let's go in the backyard and talk."

Following the swishing sound of his jeans we grab two lawn chairs and pop them open in front of his pool. Goon grabs his glasses from his white, two-pocket Guevara and slides them on to the crown of his head to hold his long black hair back. "PSHH," we open the cans of beer.

"Cheers."

"Cheers Goon. Goon, you remember when we were kids? When we were in high school. Everything was so easy, so simple. When did it all become so complicated?"

"Life changes. People change. It ain't easy Mayi."

"Remember you driving into Pearl City, in Boca, to pick up the crew. We never bullied anyone. I miss those days." We gulp our beers.

"You should think about moving back."

"I'm working on it. I just can't catch a break. Feel so stupid bro."

"Take a look at yourself. You have always been one of the smartest. You used to tutor Algebra II and Trig in high school and college. You have always been too smart for the stupid shit you do." This brings us both to break down in fits of laughter. "I'm serious! Your decisions have brought you where you are."

"Flirted my way through English with C's and D's. Was my worse subject bro but I killed it at math."

Goon crushes his beer can and stands up. "You ready for another beer?"

"Sure, why not?" While waiting for him to return I zone out staring at the orange and peach sky. Goon comes back with two more red cans and slides me a beer. We open the beers. "Cheers." We slap cans.

"Mayi, you remember when you ran away for seven days? You were seventeen and you pierced your ear without permission. Your dad was so pissed. We all had one and you wanted one so bad. You went in secret and got it done." We chuckle and sip our beers.

"Don't know what I was thinking. I could see the hurt in my pops eyes when I came back."

"Well, you know Cubans at that time. They think that's for women or gay men. So silly."

"A lot went down that year in my life. My boy Carl became a vegetable."

"Yeah, a blood clot or something?"

"It was a promotional fight night at a club. He asked me to box him that night and I refused. Our classmate Tony boxed him. I know it ate him up. In a blink, one hard punch changed both their lives. Poof. Vegetable."

"Damn Mayi! I didn't know that."

"When I think about it, I feel a little guilty. What if that had been me? That's also the year I started drinking. He died this year. Been thinking about his parents and his sister. Life is so short."

We take another gulp. "Oye!" He snaps twice. "Snap out of it. There was nothing you could have done. I certainly remember when you started drinking. You would drink out of a funnel like a jack-ass and pretend to be an elephant."

"TU TUUURUUU TUU! The royal call. High school. Good times. The end of that year I started smoking weed."

Taking a big swig of beer to work up my liquid courage, I continue. "Dog I got something to tell you. Something no one knows."

"Dale. Dime."

"I ever tell you my first sexual encounter was at eight years old?"

"What! No me lo diga?"

"I know it sounds crazy, but you know I'm no bullshitter."

He leans in. "What's up bro?"

"I slept over Cousin Lora's house in Port St. Lucie. Before going to bed she asked me if I wanted to play house. Playing house, she said now I gotta touch yours and then you touch mine. She slid her hands under the covers and my underwear and then I did it to her."

Goon looks bewildered and yells, "No way!"

Putting my hands behind my head and sighing, "Yeah. Think she was eleven or twelve. We were both kids. I'm not sure we even knew it was wrong at the time but with this divorce I have been evaluating my history with women and sex. I wonder if this is one of the reasons why I have this uncontrollable lust."

"Mayi did this happen again? Dude you're just a freak. You're a man hoe."

"It never happened again after that weekend. Look at her now, happily married."

"I know. Crazy how things work. Probably best to let it go. You guys were kids."

Pulling my sleeves down on my blazer and covering up, "Goon thanks for listening. Let's go inside. It's chilly as heck out here." We take another sip.

"Yeah Mayi. Come. Let's go in the garage. I want to show you the Saturnia marble I bought for the house."

I glance at my left wrist and my Tissot says 5:48 P.M. "Goon I love you bro. I gotta go. I told Yez, Jaxson and Ricky I'd swing by today and I still need to work."

"Yeah, dale." Goon walks me to the door and asks, "Oye, How's your pops?"

"I guess he's holding up all things considering. Don't go there to much anymore. It's too weird."

"And how's your sister?"

"I feel bad for my sister. She's living there and it can't be fun. You know we haven't spoken in over a year. It's sad. It kills me."

"Remember, you're supposed to be older and wiser. Make up with her already. It's the right thing to do."

"I know. We'll see." I give him another hug. "Sometimes it's easier said than done. Love you bro."

"Love you Mayi. Make up. Drive safe. Make that money!"

I hustle back to my car, turn on the radio and take off for Yez's house, dialing his number on the way. Talking through the Bluetooth speakers, "Yoooo…You home bro?"

"Yeah, for a little bit before New Year's. Come by now."

"That's what I was gonna do. I have to drive later. Just left Goons. See ya in ten minutes."

"O.K., dale!"

Driving through Boca, the ride is full of flash backs. While taking Camino Real to 12th Ave and heading North to Palmetto Road, I pass one palatial home after another with each street lined with palm trees and think, *"You were lucky to grow up here Mayi."* Passing the hometown favorite, Tomasso's Pizza, the smell of cheese baking wafts through my open car windows and brings a smile to my face. I pass the community center and smell the green grass that lives on the fields I played baseball on for so many years under the golden lights. Making a left immediately after the fields onto Boca Raton Blvd, I head straight and marvel at all the change this city has gone through. The old Shell gas station is now a limo service. On my left I pass my old elementary school, J.C Mitchell Elementary, where I skinned my knees on the playground often and experienced my first crush on a sweet-smiled girl with messy pigtails. Can't recall her name anymore, but I will never forget her smile. Funny, the things we remember versus the things we forget.

A few miles later I arrive at Yez's house. The ruckus from the back can be heard piercing through the jungle in his front yard. The yard is very private, with trees as high as the roof. The greenery covers the entire house from every corner. A two-person swing hangs invitingly from a huge oak tree. Chairs are dug into the gravel of the make-shift patio that may only be reached by maneuvering limestone stepping-stones on a winding path. The terrain is a bit rocky, surrounded by leaves, branches, and flowers. Green, yellow, orange, and pink petals crawl up the walls and it feels like the Garden of Eden. I duck under a few roots and knock on the door.

"KNOCK...KNOCK...KNOCK!"

Yez opens the door and greets me with his signature bark. "AR, AR, AR...AR, AR, AR, ROOT, ROOT, ROOT," he barks. "Mayis here! AR, AR...ROOT, ROOT!" He barks again. Yez has greeted everyone like this for years.

Let me absolutely take a moment to tell you about Yez and I still won't do him justice. That is 100% his calling card anywhere, anytime. No exceptions. You deal with it and we love him for it. He has always been known as Mr. Boca Raton. Anywhere he goes in this state, especially anywhere in Boca Raton, he knows someone. No exaggeration. This guy is such a big ball of energy. A big ball of fire. A daily drinker. You are guaranteed to have a hell of a good time with the Yez-Man. The women love his style and flock to him. Ricky and

I always laugh when we are out with him because he says the most absurd things, will do the craziest shit to women, in front of other women, have a big fun crazy smile doing it, and they love it. They eat that shit up. Ricky and I still can't understand how he does it. He's just being Yez. He is a free spirit and believes in peace, love and happiness. Yez sits at my height, 5'7 and 165 pounds. Great shape at forty-seven years old and bald. With my full head of hair, that is one thing I get to rub in his face on a regular basis.

Grabbing the collar of his shirt and looking for a rise out of him, "Nice pink shirt. Love the white pants. Oooh boy! Look at those pink and purple shoes. You look like a cute Rainbow Bright son." He leans in, hugs me, kisses me on the cheek and nibbles on my neck still behaving like a dog. I jump back. "Hey bro. Come on man. You always do that crap." I grin.

He shouts and laughs, "You don't like it? You can get the fuck out!" He continues laughing, ignores me, and bites my neck again.

I lean forward and give him a big hug. "How you doing bro? How's everything?"

"Everything is good Mayi! Come on. Come have a drink."

"I can't bro. I already had two with Goon. I have to drive later."

"Come on. Come have one drink."

"I'm having one drink. One drink only, you hear me, and only because it's still early."

"O.K. That's all I asked. One drink." I walk through his house, pass the jacuzzi through the swinging glass doors, to his tiki hut. To my surprise Jaxson is there.

Jaxson is the youngest of the bunch. He dresses smart.

"Hey pretty boy. You been working out? Looking jacked Jaxson."

"Put on a little muscle weight. You know, 195 now. Hit the gym buddy."

"You on juice?"

"Nah, Brah. All natural."

"You the biggest con-man this side of Texas. Who you fooling with your Jaxson Theories? Always a pleasure when I get to see all of you guys in one day. Isn't it a little cold for that outfit son?" Jaxson gets up off the wooden picnic bench and shuffles around the table. He extends his arms to hug me and shows off his pearly white commercial smile. In Jaxson fashion, he's wearing a little tank top with shorts and sandals.

"You know I'm a little more warm blooded. Hey, how's your boy?"

"He's doing O.K. He's with his mom for tonight. I had him last year at St. Augustine."

All three of us sit around the table drinking and telling old stories. The tiki hut has a TV at one end and a slew of cool novelty signs hanging on the wooden posts. I'm gazing at the lime green sign depicting a man smiling while holding out a jug of beer, "BEER…helping ugly people have sex since 1862!" when Jaxson blurts out, "We haven't hung out like this in a long time."

"Yeah Mayi, remember when you took a dump in the hallway of your dorm?" Yez shares laughingly always looking to embarrass everyone.

"Dude, hazing exists. I even had to run one mile to the school gatehouse and back butt naked in college. After a second hazing incident where I almost got in a fight, I knew it was time to leave."

Jaxson asks, "Didn't you go work at NAMB after that?"

"Yes, and I kept getting promoted there. I worked there for five years. Look one thing is for sure, with all my screw ups, I've always been a hard worker. It's the one thing I can control. Work smarter, not harder. Pay attention to detail. That's how I succeeded in baseball and that's how I live my life. All I got is my last name and my balls. I don't want you to talk bad about either. Now if I had only kept my dick in my pants back then."

"I'm going to pour us some shots." Yez gets up and takes off towards the kitchen.

As he's walking, I respond, "Not for me. I have to work soon."

"Shut the fuck up!" He nudges me and mumbles.

"Bro not for me."

Jaxson continues the conversation. "That's right. Didn't you get fired for fucking the managers?"

"They moved me from inbound to maintenance man. I was the highest paid maintenance man with very good benefits. The staff just wanted to move me away from all the ladies, not realizing they just put me in a position to hit every area of the bank. I sure did. The managers got in trouble. I was never fired but still not my best decision. I would never do that now."

"Hey guys look what the cat dragged in?" Yez shouts walking back from inside the kitchen with shots for all of us.

"What's up fellas?" Shouts Ricky walking in behind Yez.

Jaxson and I at the same time, "What's up Ricky?" We all fist pound.

"Just came to hang out before New Year's."

"Here you guys go." Yez hands out the shots.

"One of you guys are going to have to double up. I told you I'm not drinking anymore. I have to drive later."

"Shut the fuck up. Have the shot!" Yez expresses in excitement.

"Bro I told you no. Give it to Ricky. He just got here."

"What you doing for New Years?" Jaxson asks Ricky.

"Absolutely nothing. Too crazy out there. Another year has come and gone. We made it." He lights up a Marlboro 100.

"Yeah, there was a time I didn't think I'd make it to forty. Those three DUI's before twenty-five and no license for ten years. I still don't know how I made it through."

Jaxson walks to the jacuzzi laughing. "Damn, Mayi. That's when you would trike everywhere. Hop on the Tri-Rail and come down from West Palm Beach. I picked you up a few times."

Yez and Ricky simultaneously laughing, "I remember that."

"Dude, I payed a lot of money. Had to do eleven weekends in the stockade. Getting around was hell but I'd get up at 5 A.M. to trike thirteen miles to work. Did it every day. Always had to have a book bag with a change of clothes. Getting the DUI's actually saved my life. I thank God for that. Really woke me up."

Ricky interrupts, "Here you go with religion again."

"No, No. I'm not going to get into it. You see the teal and blue sign here to the right. It says Beach Rules. Unwind, Relax and Enjoy. We ain't getting into it today brother." I reply.

Ricky jumps back in. "The three-year stripper!" Everyone bursts out in laughter.

I defend myself. "I had to. My parents weren't paying me shit at the store, but I loved it. Those freaky ladies couldn't get enough of it. They are just as cheap as Jaxson. I made $100 just to show up. Then at least $50 in tips. Dancing for twenty minutes."

"HA, HA, HA, HA …HA, HA, HA, HA." They continue laughing. Then they taunt.

"Go Mayi. Go Mayi. Let's see it."

Peeling the label off my beer to distract me from their heckling. "Guys shut the fuck up. My dancing days are over." I take a sip of my beer. "While we are being honest, I never went to Spain. I had to do thirty days of jail time or get credit for jail time if I attended an intake facility for thirty days. I attended Carp intake. My parents didn't want any of you to know."

Jaxson snaps, "Oh my God. I remember that. You're telling me you didn't go to Spain?"

Yez adds in. "Yeah dog. You weren't in Spain?"

I smile. "Nope! Never been. I'm sure it's nice this time of year."

Yez stands up. "Who's ready for another beer?"

Jaxson and Ricky, "I am!"

I look around and stand up, sauntering to one of the poles that holds the tiki hut up. There is a white sign dangling off of it that reads, "RANCHO BAR." "But you know what I regret the most? I regret not doing juice in high school. Everyone was juicing. Some of my doubles would have been gone and I would have had more home runs. Things might have been different."

Ricky plays an air violin. "Cry me a river."

I point up to the Rancho Bar sign and ask Ricky to read the tag line.

"A NIGHT AT RICKYS' PRICELESS." He reads out loud.

I laugh. "You're an ass. You're not giving me a priceless time bro."

Yez comes back with the beers and hands them out.

Ricky continues, "Things might have been different. You might not even have that awesome son you have now. You could be in a wheelchair or a vegetable. You ever think of that?"

Jaxson is sitting next to the pole I'm leaning against, so I tap him on his shoulder. "Watch this Jaxson, watch…Yeah. When God gave me my boy; that was the second time he saved my life."

Ricky turns to walk inside and throws his hands up in the air. "Oh brother!" Yez follows him in.

I tap Jaxson again laughing, "What I tell ya?" I sit back on the picnic bench.

Jaxson asks, "No chance for you and your wife?"

I sigh. "Don't think so bro. Ignored a lot of flags. Her temper. The conflict with my son. I thought it would change when I bought the townhouse, but it never did. She still complained over everything and I mean everything. It was miserable. I didn't want to go home. We just never gelled as a family. I think it was rushed and not sanctioned by God. We had a lot of cards stacked against us. We had huge issues before we even got married but she couldn't wait and I ignored the signs."

"Mayi, you know I love you. Whatever happens, I'm here for you."

"Thanks Jaxson. It's getting late. Gotta work. Come inside with me to say bye to these two clowns."

We shut the glass door behind us. Yez and Ricky are in the kitchen standing around the white and black granite counter tops.

"Hey guys happy New Year. I have to go. Don't want to be out later than one or two tonight." Opening the front door, I turn around and raise my pointer finger in a tisk-tisk sway back and forth. "Ya'll need Jesus. You all need Jesus. Hope you have a great 2020."

The New Year's rush of rides goes by quick and easy. There are only two that I find memorable. I'm in the middle of nowhere in Miramar and I have gone to two gas stations in need of a rest stop. "Hey, can I use your bathroom?"

"No. It's out of order."

"Damn it!"

With no other option, I drive to the first dark alley and find a dumpster. I've done this so many times in an alley or a parking lot. Turning off my car and positioning myself between the car and the dumpster, I look left. I look right. I make sure no one is around and unzip. "Aaahhhh." Before zipping up, the phone is already receiving another fare. "BILILING, BILILING, BILILING!" The call is half a mile away and after being on the road for three hours my haul is $163 for the night.

I arrive at the pick-up address, hop out, open and close the doors. "THUMP, THUMP!" I slide back in the driver's seat and confirm. "John?"

John is easily in his 70's wearing a suit and tie. His companion is of Asian descent and is easily in her early to mid 30's. She is wearing an elegant light purple one shoulder dress. Her long jet black hair falls straight down her back.

"Yes sir. Mayi?"

"Yes sir. How you guys doing tonight?"

John and the young lady respond, "Great and yourself?"

"Not too bad. Almost done. Might do one more after you guys and call it."

John yawns, "Aah, busy tonight?" He runs his hand through his salt and pepper hair.

I peak in the rearview. "Yes, as a matter of fact it has been. That's why I'm almost done. If it's hot or windy and you want the windows up just let me know."

The young lady responds. "Can you please roll up the windows, but leave the sunroof open?"

"Absolutely. Done."

"You think we can make it to the Hard Rock by midnight?" John asks.

"I seriously doubt it. It will be cutting it close. Depends on traffic. The GPS shows we are twenty-four minutes away from the casino and its seventeen minutes until the ball drops. You're asking me to cut seven minutes of time. Are you giving me permission to speed?"

"Yes, we are."

"I will do my best."

I throw on Shakira, "Hips Don't Lie" and accelerate like a bat out of hell. The song drowns out the noise in the back a little, but I can still hear and don't look back. The sound of sloppy kisses is mixed in with the passengers, "Ooh's" and "Aah's." The life of a rideshare driver is never dull. I hop on I-75 North and punch it. The speedometer passes ninety miles per hour as I merge onto I-595 east bound. The green exit signs fly by. "Flamingo Road, Hiatus Road, Nob Hill Road," the list continues until reaching the 441 South exit.

"We have a chance to make it on time for New Year's. It will depend on the traffic." The tires screech as I make a hard right onto the exit and punch the gas one more time. The night erupts in color accompanied by loud booms.

"BANG, BANG, POP, POP, BOOM, BOOM, HISS, HISS, CRACKLE, CRACKLE, CRACKLE!"

The girl shouts, "Look! Look at all the pretty colors."

The reds, whites, blues and golds are popping and screeching while scattering across the dark black sky. Upon twinkling away, a cloud of dust lingers in the air.

The clock on the dash reads 11:55 P.M. The passengers are enjoying the premature light show. I'm cruising fifty-eight in a forty-five-zone hoping to get lucky with green lights. Hard Rock is a good fastball throw away, but I have to pump the breaks. The herd of cars wrap all the way out to 441 just past the light at the entrance at Seminole Way. I turn around. "Guys, I'm sorry. I tried. If you walk from here, you're a good ten minutes away from the Hard Rock. You may get hot and sweaty. Or we can spend New Year's together. There's two minutes left. The choice is yours."

John has his right arm around her shoulder kissing her neck. "I think we will spend it together. We are here. No reason to rush anymore."

I turn back around. "At least I won't be alone this year. Hey, Happy 2020 you two. I wish you a prosperous year."

"Same to you." John replies.

"BILILING, BILILING, BILLIING!" Another call comes in before I drop them off and I accept. Before arriving to the drop off point John says, "Hey, I heard you say you're alone. Come party with us tonight. No one should be alone on New Year's."

"John, I would love to, but I just picked up another ride. The pick-up is actually here. I'm going to do this ride and call it a night. Appreciate the offer." Pulling up under the casino's bright lights I stop the car. "Now give me a moment and let me get those doors for you."

While we shake hands goodbye he slides me a twenty and says, "Here. You deserve this. Thanks for the great driving. You should race NASCAR. Drive safe tonight."

"Thank you. Don't have too much fun. Win a lot of money."

I turn around and on the other side of my car is a brunette, slouched over, hair all over the place, black top with white shorts, white heels and her purse tangled in her arm looking like a hot mess staring. I ask, "Lidia?"

"Maaayiiii?"

"Yes ma'am. Let me get that door for you." I run around my car and open the door and close it, "THUMP!" I run around to the other side, get in the car and confirm. "3298 N.W. 6th Ave., Boca Raton?"

"Yees sure Maayii." She confirms slurring and mumbling. I close the sunroof and point the A.C vent directly on her to dry off her perspiration. Her head is bobbing around. Purse items like her wallet and lipstick litter the backseat. Marvin Gay, "Let's get it on" is playing lightly. As I hop on I-95, I hear snoring louder than bear cubs hibernating.

I pull off the Glades Road exit East and make an immediate left onto Airport Road heading north. Driving on the winding road, Lidia comes back to life. "Hey, we are almo-brgg-st ho-brgg-me."

"Lidia are you O.K.? Do you want me to pull over? I'm in no rush. I can pull over if you need me to."

"No. I'm O.K brrg-Mayi." Gagging while she taps on my right shoulder, "Go, Go. I'm-" She lifts her shirt over her face. "Brrrggg... Brrrggg!"

"I told you I would ha-"

"Brrrggg...Brrrggg...Brrrggg." She continues to throw up into her shirt.

"-have pulled over so you can throw up." I roll down the windows. The sour stench fills my car. Twenty more seconds. All I needed was twenty more seconds and we arrive at her house.

More awake with chunks of throw up all over her shirt and in her hair. "I'm sorry. I didn't mean to throw up in your car. I thought I could make it."

"It's ok hun. It happens. Let me get that door for you."

"Oh, no. You don't have to."

"It's O.K. I insist. I get to stretch out my legs."

I walk out, open and close the door, "THUMP!"

"Lidia, Happy New Year. Hope you feel better."

"Happy New Year and thank you."

"No worries. It's my job."

I run back in my car, lower the windows and hurry to the Exxon station on 2nd Ave. and Yamato Rd. with my nose in my shirt. A flashback pops up from the night I totaled my car. Same gas station. I open the back door and see chunks of red and orange all over my seats and on my floor mats. Reaching forward from the back seat into the center console I grab a stack of napkins. Wiping the seats down and laughing, *"It wasn't as bad as it could have been. She took a lot of it with her shirt, thank God."* I walk inside the station and purchase a Black Ice Christmas tree and hang it to hide the foul smell.

Looking down at the Tissot, it's 1:23 A.M. Via text, with a picture of vomit attached, the rideshare company is made aware of the incident. Turning the car on and lowering all the windows fully, I begin my trek back home by reflecting on the night.

"I don't want to end up like John. Seventy years old and ordering prostitutes. That sucks and so does starting 2020 with throw up in my car. I hope it's not a sign of what's to come."

In my lonesome, I pray out loud. "God, I thank you for what you have given me and for what you haven't. I thank you for everyone you have brought in and out of my life. I pray that you help my aching heart. Don't give up on me. Please protect those who need it, save those who seek it and help those less fortunate. Thank you for letting me see another glorious day. Thank you for my daily bread. Lord, please help me with my lust and this generational curse. Am I a product of my family? Am I destined for more? Please don't let me end up like John. I pray for his soul. In the name of Jesus Christ, I pray that you show me signs and forgive me for my earthly sins, Amen."

MATTHEW 25: 41-46

PART I: 43 Texts to Royalty

The book of Matthew, verse 41 reads: "Then he will say to those on his left, depart from me, you who are cursed, into the eternal fire prepared for the devil and his angels. 42 For I was hungry, and you gave me nothing to eat, I was thirsty, and you gave me nothing to drink, 43 I was a stranger, and you did not invite me in. I needed clothes and you did not clothe me. I was sick and in prison and you did not look after me."

44 "They also will answer, Lord, when did we see you hungry or thirsty or a stranger or needing clothes or sick or in prison, and did not help you?"

45 "He will reply, Truly I tell you, whatever you did not do for the least of these, you did not do for me."

46 "Then they will go away to eternal punishment, but the righteous to eternal life."

This is the verse that almost did me in. The verse that almost landed me in serious trouble. I caution you to use wisdom and intelligence when exercising this verse and not act loosely as I have.

The next eight months are the rollercoaster ride of a lifetime, coupled with loop-de-loops, spins, falls, and twists. Right when I thought I was done with the ride, I realize it's just the first lap.

The ride began February 5 2020, 7:39 P.M. I am driving and re-playing highlights of the wonderful vacation to Las Vegas my wife and I returned from January 20th. Tickets were purchased prior to our separation as a birthday gift for her. She was adamant she wasn't going to go and at the last minute changed her mind. I had to cancel on my cousin and felt horrible about it. I would never do that again.

We went to the Grand Canyon, Hoover Dam and stayed at The Venetian hotel on the strip. We went on a gondola ride through the mall. Only in Vegas.

We strolled the strip, visited a weed dispensary and even gambled a little. The mountain views were breath taking with the white snowy peaks. I was totally head over heels for her again and thought we were going to work things out. She looked at me in a way I had not felt in a long time. It was our first successful vacation together.

God lets no bad deed go unpunished. He has ways of reaching us. Whether that deed occurred in the past or future, He sees and knows everything before you have even thought about it.

Still driving my head bobs side to side to Jay Z, "Dirt off Your Shoulder." I turn the knob down to the left and grab my phone. I turn off my apps and dial the wife.

"Hey, how are you?"

"I'm well and yourself?" She asks.

"Well, I'm calling to see if you want me to set up that trip to Hawaii we talked about? It's free. We may as well go."

"Sure. Why not? It should be fun. Hey, did you check the diamond club timeshare papers?"

"Not yet. We just got back."

"Ugg, what are you waiting for?"

Laughing through the phone, "I'm calling to set up a trip to Hawaii and you're busting my balls about that right now. I told you, it will get done. Motherfucker, I can't win one. Don't worry. That will get done."

"O.K, please do."

"Alright, I gotta go."

I complete three more rides. At 9:01 P.M. a text alert comes in from my wife. We have been communicating more since the trip and I am feeling excited. I save all our texts, even after the separation I wasn't ready to let them go. *"-You left a bitter taste calling me motherfucker. I don't appreciate you cursing at me. You might think it's ok since you are so use to talking that way but I'm not nor will ever be.-"*

I pull off into a gas station, grab my phone and turn my apps off again. I text back. *"-Man, I called to set up a trip to Hawaii and all you got out of it was one word? What is wrong with you? Why do you always pick out negative stuff for no reason? You said it yourself. That I'm used to talking that way and I am working on it. Isn't going to change overnight. Look, I only used one curse word. That's an improvement. You know I was trying to do something nice and loving.-"*

My attempt at humor fails and she replies, *"-I love you but there are times that you leave me with a sense of regret and confusion, but you know you're my weakness and you reel me back in to accept it all once again. The bad, the negative. Making me hate myself for it. All I want is a partner to love me, to be there for me to grow old with and I wish that could be you, but I feel that you're not in it. It's not what you want.-"*

My fingers are heating up. *"-We are different, but I haven't been trying to reel you back in. You always know how to ruin a good day and a good thing. I knew sooner or later your mind and anxiety would get the best of you. Where you're wrong is that I do want to grow old with you and be your partner but being your partner consists of a lot harder work than it should. I don't want to spend the rest of my life arguing with you over stupid shit because of your anxiety. Maybe we should just move on and go our separate ways. Regret, confusion, reel you back in, bad, negative, make you hate yourself. Wow you make me sound amazing. Maybe I should let you find that partner you're seeking because I don't think it's me.-"*

My heart aches and longs for her. The back and forth is unbearable. Love is pain and hurts, that I understand. Shouldn't love also spring hope and positivity?

She sends back, *"-Don't care to waste my time sharing my feelings since you can't handle it nor do you care to hear my thoughts.-"*

My thumbs and fingers are moving quickly again. *"-You always circle to the same feelings. Don't you see it will always be something?-"*

This is the only woman to ever take me out of my element other than the mother of my only child. It's night. The mental anguish evaporates any chance of me continuing to work. My mind and apps go dark. *"I can't believe this chick is so mental all she could think of was the word motherfucker when I called to set up a trip to Hawaii! We are just too different. I can't believe it. I can't believe what that call turned into. Have I been in denial? This must be the sign I prayed for. I guess You give us what we need, not what we want."*

We don't speak again until I reach out that Saturday by text at 4:38 P.M.

"-You going to church today or tomorrow?-"

"-Why does it matter? Trying to avoid me again?-"

"-I don't have a choice. I have to go today so I can play my baseball game tomorrow.-"

"-So why ask me then? Or are you hoping to see me?-"

"-Nope!-"

Texts fly sporadically until Valentine's Day. In a moment of weakness, I text, *"-Just wanted to tell you I love you and Happy Valentine's Day. I hope you have a nice day.-"*

"-Thanks. Same to you.-"

I know I haven't been to the townhome since September but want to do something nice for her. I get ready and rush over to the flower shop.

"Hi. Do you have some purple and white orchids?"

"You're actually in luck. I have a few and can put an arrangement together for you."

"Awesome. I'll take it. Where are your cards?"

"They are right around the corner," as the attendant points to the rear right corner of the shop. I spin the card rack looking for just the right message while she prepares the floral arrangement. Once ready, I rush out of there. I'm bobbing and weaving to her house making one last stop to get Lindell chocolates.

I arrive and hear the familiar bark of Oakley. Dropping the gifts at my side and kneeling to pet her, I coo. "God, I missed you girl. My Baby. My Oakley! You're a good girl! Yeah! Papi loves you!" She's rubbing her noise all over me and her tail is spanking the air. Tears creep up and I dip out quickly. *"I can't keep doing this."*

A text pops up at 6:39 P.M.

"-Thanks for the flowers, candy and card. Hope you had a great day as well.-"

Thinking it through, *"Wow. Both texts sucked. Don't over-react. I'm sure we are both hurting."* We did not see each other that weekend. The following Tuesday, she calls me and asks, "Hey, can I come over?"

"I'm not sure that's a great idea."

"Please! I miss you. Don't you miss me?"

"Of course, I miss you. You know I love you and will for a while. You know what you do to me. This could hurt me. Hurt us."

"Come on. One last time. Don't you want to feel me?"

"O.K. Come over." Yup, just like that.

She lives fifteen minutes away and arrives quickly. "KNOCK... KNOCK!"

I rush to the door and she pushes her way past me. She's wearing a trench coat and opens it up proudly before I can even shut the door.

"Wow! That's all you wore here. The coat and the white lingerie?" She's grinning from ear to ear, with her cute giggle, nodding yes and throws me on my grey couch as I say, "Wow! You are so sexy! I love you!"

"I love you, too!" She devours me.

This starts a vicious cycle. Tuesday, Thursday. Sometimes both days and sometimes one. We were both vulnerable and the random sex continues for some time. For two weeks things between us were going better, though nothing was concrete. We remain officially separated. Dispersed over the days, I receive a text here, a sexy photo there, but never a call.

On Leap Day I wake up at 5 A.M to get dressed for work. I slide my gyms shorts on and a black hoodie over my head. After four hours, my last ride brings me to the beach at Palm Beach Island. I park to observe the sunny cool day for twenty minutes, tasting the salt in the air, while strolling along the sandy sidewalk.

After the walk, I drive over to Havanas to warm up with my morning coffee. The girls at the counter are sharing their usual gossip when one mentions that her friend is pregnant. She says, "The guy said her IUD was hitting him during sex, so she had it removed and BAM!" She snaps her fingers. "Now she's pregnant." Margerita says, "Pregnant is better than crazy. I had to get mine removed because it was making me hormonal. I couldn't get through the day without crying or yelling."

Thinking this may be helpful information, I text my wife.

"-Hey, I heard your IUD maybe pumping hormones into you. I would look into that. See if maybe it causes you to snap. Just sayin, look into it.-"

A text pings in immediately, *"-Really? You are still trying to justify and blame me for my actions instead of looking into yours. I am not on birth control nor does my IUD have hormones so no it was not me being hormonal!-"*

"-I'm not justifying anything dumb ass. I was trying to help you as a suggestion, but I guess some people will never change. Have a

great rest of your weekend. Looking forward to the day all our ties are over.-"

I get back to my car and head home and a text comes in. At the red light on 10th Ave. and Dixie Highway I grab my phone and take a peek.

"-Wow and there you go again with the insults. You will never change. The divorce papers are already filled out. All that is needed is your signature with the notary.-"

I text back quickly before the light turns green.

"-Leave them there. I'll pick them up and drop them off. I'm not goin' back to the courthouse. So, you're not hormonal? You're just naturally nasty. Good to know.-" The light turns green and I continue south to 6th Ave. and make a right heading to congress when, "BING!" A text comes in.

"-You just don't get it and never understood. No one likes to feel disrespected, but you felt that it's normal to do so. How can you possibly think of making someone happy when you're not happy with yourself. You only project your misery. So let's be done with it!-"

I feel my anxiety level rise. I speed up on to Congress until I get home. Once home I stay in the car with the A.C. on and respond.

"-Be done with what? The marriage has been done for a while, right? Funny thing is I was actually trying to help you but as usual you take everything as a personal attack. I really do hope you can find someone who can make you happy because I never could. What hurts me the most is I really thought we were going to get back together after Vegas. I really wanted to but then you trip out over the word motherfucker. The issue is everything and anything is a disrespect to you because you're so fucking anal and focus on the bullshit instead of what's important. You feel disrespected because of your ego and pride or you wouldn't feel that way. I'm the happiest I've been in three years now that I'm not in that house with you. Good luck fighting with all the guys when they say something you don't like. No one has ever felt disrespected by the way I talk except you.-"

"-Mayi you say you love me but then hurt me with the things you say.-"

"-Man you broke me with the motherfucker when I was calling to set up this dream vacation. I don't know how you couldn't see how hard I was trying to get back with you and work this out!-"

I get out of my car and finally walk in and lay on my bed. I'm having a text war with my wife. She chimes back.

"-That's the thing. You only see how you feel but not how you do me so disrespectfully.-"

"-Dude you say hurtful things too. Do you love me? Or did you love me? I don't remember being the one who said they were out of love. Why I stayed is beyond me. I wish you the best. I guess we will always have the Vegas trip. I started falling for you hard there again. The memories there and the fact that I was able to make you laugh and smile one last time I will cherish.-"

"-Not sure if you had these but wanted to share the pics of our trip to Vegas.-"

The pics of Vegas comes in like daggers through my heart and she knows I will feel the pain. My pillowcases are getting wet. I'm wiping tears off with my shirt. I sob, *"Man do I love her. Man, I'm sad. Why don't we work?"*

She chimes in again.

"-Since you have the time why don't you go back and read all the text you have sent me and see who snaps at who and who is nasty by the nature and blows things way out of proportion like usual to make things 100 times worse too there's point of no return? That why we are where we are today! Then you say have a great day. That's malicious.-"

"-Oh no. There are a lot of reasons why we are where we are today to the point of no return. It really started when you said you were out of love. But listen, I don't need to read texts or keep reliving this.-"

"-You can't ever take any responsibility for your actions.-"

"-I hope someday we can be friends but that's years from now and a big hope because I seriously doubt it. Oh, I can take responsibility. It's obvious you can't.-"

"-You haven't.-" She insists.

"-It's always the blame game between both of us. You haven't changed either. You still blame me for everything!-"

"-Mayi sharing my feelings has been a sin for you which you can't handle.-"

"-Remember what Conny England said. The feelings that you share are always negative. Listen I don't want to do this anymore today. Leave me the papers and I'll pick them up and have them notarized. Stop this. We are 100% over, right? So there is no more point going back and forth.-"

"-For sure.-"

I get red and hot, and I'm offended. I fire back again. My ego was not satisfied with that answer.

"-Everything I do was always malicious towards you or your kids. That's what was always in your mind and how was I supposed to continue living like that? I've been nothing but good and generous to you and even giving you 16k out of 24k and the house. Your still sour.-"

"-Mayi You can't even apologize for all the things you have said to intentionally hurt me because your feelings are hurt as usual.-"

I get up and walk to the kitchen. I fix myself a glass of water as my phone chimes again.

"-Just own up to your shit for once.-"

"-Pot calling the kettle black. You have apologized to me zero times in four years. All I was for you was a safe and secure roof for you and your kids when your lease was up. You wouldn't have snapped at me for everything if you loved me. You would have had patience. I have tried to deal with the trauma your first marriage caused you. You claim victim and started 98% of our fights. Your argument is that I should have handled it better. Maybe you shouldn't have started every fucking fight over your feelings that change and are usually

negative. Yeah, let's blame me. Look in the mirror. You have pushed two husbands away. You only loved yourself and your kids!-"

I sit back on the couch, slam my cup of water and droplets spill on the white desk. Another text comes in.

"-Again, you're only trying to justify your actions with mine. Once again finding the blame on me or whatever reason. I react to all your BS and negativity. Just stop already and take accountability for your own actions. Did you actually think that I would tolerate all your insults and offenses for the sake of being a good wife? I'm sure that's what you thought but all these years you should've known I am not one to stay quiet when I know I deserve your respect and am worth more than how you treated me.-"

"-You were never a good wife. You think I was supposed to tolerate your abuse? You started every fight. I'm the one tolerating. Do you see your argument is I should have reacted better, but my reaction didn't matter. I walk away, I'm abandoning you. I slap your ass and be playful and I'm not taking it seriously and you get mad. You're so confrontational about everything!-"

"-I've never abused you or even talked to you the way you have to me. So disrespectfully disgusting and evil intent to hurt me with your words. Now that's verbal abuse that I always got from you since the beginning and yet you don't want to take any responsibility for your actions playing the victim like a true narcissist. Stop trying. It ain't working in your favor.-"

"-I don't want anything to do with you. Never mind, leave me alone and I'll leave you alone. It's the same circle. It's 11 A. M. and we have been at it since 9:43.-"

Distraught, barely able to catch my breath, I stomp out of my apartment back in my car to drive again. Sitting behind the wheel and listening to other people's issues can be therapeutic for me. The third ride of my day is a middle aged, well-built blonde with light green eyes, slender and tall. Her bright red and yellow dress accentuate her long legs. I speed walk to open the passenger rear door and confirm, "Ms. Kennedy?"

"Yes. That's me." "THUMP!" I close the door and rush back in the car confirming the address. "Yes, that's right." She answers.

"If it's cold or windy and you want the windows up just let me know."

Her dimples flair up. "No, it's perfect. The day is gorgeous. That why I love Florida. Hey it's Mayi, right?"

"Yes, Ma'am it is."

"Mayi can I hire you for the day?"

"What did you have in mind?"

"We can do this ride and finish it. I'll pay you cash for the next few hours. I have a few things I have to do."

"O.K. I can do that. How many stops? Where are they? And about for how long?"

"I have to make a few more stops and then home. One stop is in Boca. Home is not where you picked me up though. It's well after twelve now. How does about fifty an hour sound? I'll give you $150 until 3:30 P.M."

"Deal. I grew up in Boca and always go down there so no problem. We are almost at the stop for the app."

She leans back. "Thank you."

"No worries. It's my job."

She walks in and out of our first stop, a nutrition center, and comes back with a small bottle of hydrogen water and a white bag filled with different vitamin bottles. Waiting for her at the passenger rear door, I open it with flare. "Oh, a gentleman. I'm getting first class service today. I feel like I'm in a limo."

"Part of the service." "THUMP!" I get back in the driver's seat.

She says, "Let's go to Boca."

I plug an office address into my GPS and throw my shades over my eyes. "Let's rock and roll. We are out west so 441 South is the best shot. Not too many lights until you reach Boca. That's the route I'm taking."

"O.K, I trust you know the routes best."

We stop at the Lantana Road light. "Mayi you're pretty light on the eyes? How old are you?"

"Thank you. I'm forty-two. Forty-three in July."

"Wow, you look great! I thought you were thirty-four or thirty-five. You work out?"

The light turns green, I grip the wheel and accelerate. I glance in the mirror, "Yes ma'am I do. You know if you eat right, work out, drink a lot of water and get your rest, it will keep you looking younger and healthy. I truly believe that."

"Well, it certainly is working for you."

I blush and grin, "Thank you."

This happens all the time in my car and I divert the attention. "Oh, this is a great song. Let me play it up for you." I turn up the radio to Lionel Richie, "Say you, Say me." I look down and my speedometer reads sixty-five. A few songs later we arrive at the building on 441.

"I'll be right back. Just picking something up from my lawyer."

"O.K. give me a minute, let me get that door."

"Wow. Thank you."

"My pleasure. I'll be here."

She takes a little longer than expected so I get back in my car to check something on the phone. Distracted by my RobinHood app and checking my Bitcoin she surprises me and opens the front passenger side door, hops in the seat and reclines back to give herself more leg room. Looking at me with her bright green eyes and smiling she says, "I hope you don't mind. You seemed cool enough to sit up here. Is that O.K.?" She bats her eyelashes.

I turn and look to my right and make eye contact. "No, it's cool. No worries. I don't feel threatened by you. I mean, you're not going to kill me or anything. It's O.K. Where to next?" I start to travel north on 441.

"Well remember, I am a real Kennedy. I'm sure your murder would make the news." We laugh and my eyes open a little wider watching the road. "One more stop and then home. I'm hungry. Let's go to Bennys on the Beach in Lake Worth. I got it."

"You sure?"

"Yes, it's fine. Here let me give you this now." She pulls out an envelope and hands me five $20's and a $50.

"You're more than generous and you're paying for lunch. This is way too much. Take forty back." I try to hand her the money back, but she insists.

"No, it's O.K. I want you to have it."

"Listen, I don't rip people off. I'm keeping one hundred ten. Please keep forty towards lunch. I wouldn't feel comfortable."

"A man with integrity also." She declares.

"You give me too much credit. You don't even know me." I have a hard time listening to her compliments when my wife feels the complete opposite.

"Well, I know you seem like a very nice and sweet man. I also know other people would have taken all the money. I also think you look so much more beautiful from up here." She brushes her hand on my right arm and I don't move it away.

"Ma'am if I-"

"And stop calling me ma'am, it's Ms. Kennedy."

"O.K... Ms. Kennedy, if I didn't know any better, I would think you're flirting with me." I make a right on Lake Worth Rd and head east towards Benny on the Beach.

"You're just figuring that out. Is it working?" She leans closer. "Mmm. You smell good too. I could eat you. What are you wearing?"

I can't help but peek out of the corner of my eye and check her out from head to toe. "I'm wearing Chrome by Azaro. So, you're a real Kennedy, huh?"

As she gathers her hair up into a pony-tail and answers, "Yup. That was my lawyer earlier. I had to pick up some money from him. He holds it in an escrow for me."

We arrive at Bennys and sit by the pier. Over crab cakes and eggs benedict we exchange short stories. She is a huge conspiracy theorist. We leave Bennys and at my car I ask her, "Front or back?"

"Front." I open and close the door, "THUMP!" Before I can even push the "start" button on the car, she jumps across from the front passenger seat, smacks my lips and starts making out with me. I don't stop her, kissing her right back.

The feeling is different than with the ring toss bandit that stole my car. For one thing, I'm sober. For another, my marriage is officially over. Lastly, I am falling into lust and breaking my most important rule of rideshare; don't hook up with clients. The good and the bad battle in my heart. One thing is leading to another and she stops to look at me with catty eyes and a seductive grin. She demands, "Take me home. I want you to come home with me."

Despite never having a prior sexual encounter with a rider, though many have attempted, I give up. I have no strength left. Mumbling and smooching, "O.K....Give me... the address for my...ah, ah...GPS?"

The next twenty-five-minute ride was tough. Twenty-five minutes to think and digest the situation. *"Do I? Don't I?"* The tug of war with the flesh. Her hand is running through my hair, down my neck and rubbing my upper back. *"How can I deny her? I haven't been home since October. It's totally over. Not once has she asked me to come back home. So why not? She is a Kennedy after all. If I'm gonna break a rule, may as well be with American royalty."*

We arrive, park and I turn towards her. "You already know you have to let me get the door." With fleetness of foot, I open and close the door, "THUMP!" Like a lost puppy I follow her in. The place is huge and elegantly decorated in a mixture of antique wood and modern art. I walk across the rustic chevron rug, admiring family photos that hang along the walls in matching oak frames of all sizes.

"Would you like some water?"

"Please. I am thirsty." While in the kitchen, she grabs a cup from the cabinet above, fills it with ice water and hands it to me. She holds onto one ice cube in her fingers and runs it down her chest between her breasts. The water drips down her chest and she grabs me around my shoulders and pulls me in for another kiss. We passionately kiss and Ms. Kennedy continues to stare through me with her shinning green eyes.

"Follow me," she says and grabs my hand. She leads the way to her bedroom.

"Where's your bathroom?" I ask.

"First door on the right when you walk out."

"Thank you. Be right back." I walk in the bathroom over to the white vanity and wash my hands. I wash my face and look in the mirror. I interrogate myself. *"We really doing this right now? We can still leave."* The man in the mirror is reckless, hurt, distraught, confused on the verge of a breakdown. I pull myself together ready to leave, but the red lingerie laying on the bed in the shape of a figure eight stops me. Lust wins.

She has protection on the night table to the right. I casually make my way over to the bed and grab the condom. After some caressing, I took her. I felt a little off. A little awkward. It had been the first time with another woman, sober. It was what I call "hate sex." No emotion. Just dogged her, but not a jerk in the process. Afterward, though I didn't care, I asked, "So how long are you here for?"

"About a week. Can I hire you for one more morning? I have a few things I have to do before I leave." She caresses the tattoo on my right arm.

"Sure. Just make sure you let me know the day before so I can schedule it."

"What does the tattoo say? Looks Tribal."

"My guy did a great job. I wanted it to look tribal but it's actually mine and my son's initials. Look closely."

"Ahh, I see it now. I'm probably going to hire you Wednesday or Thursday."

"Yeah, no worries." We fondle each other for a bit longer and I stop before anything can heat up again. "Hey I gotta go. I'm gonna work a little more this evening but I'll see you this week. Give me a pen so I can give you my number."

She rolls over to her night table and reaches for a pen and paper in the drawer. Reciting my number one digit off, on purpose, I have already made the decision not to see her again.

"Remember, call or text me the day before."

"O.K., I got it."

I get up and get dressed. She lays around in the red lace lingerie that no longer holds power over me. She walks me to the door, waves goodbye and I run to the car to turn on my apps. Driving towards my apartment the sun is setting.

At 9 P.M. I accept the last ride of my night. "BILILING, BILILING, BILILING!" A ride for "DETROIT" comes in. I maneuver to the pick-up spot in Lucerne Lakes off Lake Worth Rd. Arriving early, there is no one around. I get out of my car, "THUMP," and walk over to the rear passenger side door and stretch out my legs while admiring the cool night sky. "Detroit" walks out with two suitcases and is a total hot mess. 5'9 brunette, hair flowing everywhere, but pretty, like a lost lamb. She is wearing a dress dotted all over with tulips, roses and sunflowers. She struggles with the suitcases.

"Detroit?"

"Yes, Mayi?"

"Yes. Would you like help with those suitcases?"

"Please. Could you? While you do that, I'll check your tag?"

"143 CNL, I got your suitcases, no worries." I head over to her suitcases. She looks at my tag to make sure it matches the app. I load the suitcases into the trunk and close the door for her, "THUMP!"

"Thank you Mayi. That was awfully nice of you. Not many drivers load our suitcases. It's nice to be treated like a lady."

"Yeah, that's just the way I was raised. You do little things like that. I don't know. It just makes sense. Let me confirm with you. We are headed to Palm Beach International, PBI?"

"Yes sir. Can you get there in twenty minutes? My flight leaves in thirty-five minutes."

"I'm not sure I can get there in twenty minutes from here. Even if I do, I don't think you're getting on that flight. Why did you wait for the last minute to order your ride?"

"I wasn't ready and then when I was, I had two guys get lost, not make it and cancel." She sweeps her hair into a bun and I step on the gas.

"What are you going to do if you don't make it? I think you should start planning for not making it. Maybe a flight tomorrow because I know PBI is shutting down soon."

"If I don't make it, I can always just go back where you picked me up and leave tomorrow. I'd really like to make this flight."

"I wish I could guarantee you do. I'm pretty sure you won't. What's with Detroit. You from there or something?"

"Yes sir. I'm from Detroit, Michigan but right now I live in Flynt."

"Yeah. They had a water issue over there didn't they? They got sued for contaminating the water or something?"

"Yes, that's exactly it. Thank God I just got there and hopefully just a stop."

I look in the rearview. "If it's cold or windy and you want the windows up, just let me know."

"No. It's a wonderful night. Great weather."

"I hear ya. I love it." I find G-Unit on my playlist because I know she's from Detroit.

"Yeah, I love that. Leave that there Mayi!"

I raise up the volume. The moon is full and lights the night sky. The air is thick and chilly. We arrive at the airport.

Pulling up to departures, I say, "I don't think you're going to make this flight in ten minutes."

"Mayi can I have your number in case I don't make it? I'd rather have you drive me back. I'll pay you like twenty bucks."

"Sure, no worries. Plug it in 561-555-5555. I'll go to the Wawa and wait about twenty minutes. If I haven't heard from you, you made it."

"O.K. awesome. You're such a sweetheart."

"Yeah. Simple. Give me a moment. Let me get that door for you." I run to the rear passenger door because the people working at the airports are so rude. I open and close the door, "THUMP!" Open the trunk and unload her suitcases.

She hands me $5. "Thank you. In case I don't see you again."

"No worries. My pleasure." Close my trunk, "THUMP!" Drive across the street to a Wawa gas station and let five minutes pass by. "RING, RING, RING!"

"Hello?"

"Hello Mayi. It's Detroit. Can you come get me please? I rescheduled for six tomorrow morning."

"I'll be right there. I'm across the street." I pick up Detroit and we are heading back.

"Hey Mayi, you mind stopping at a gas station so I can grab a six-pack?"

"That's cool. There's a few on the way."

"You are so nice. Pretty cute, too. How old are you? Like thirty?"

I think, *"Oh, brother here we go. Mayi we don't need any more trouble."*

Replying to her question, "That's flattering. I'll be forty-three in July. I know it's rude to ask a lady, but you asked me. How old are you?"

Her face turns red and her cheeks blush. "You look great for forty-three. I don't feel so bad anymore. I'm fifty-one."

"You look great for fifty-one. I thought you were about my age." I smile at her through the rearview mirror. "Why would you feel bad?"

"Ahem...Because I thought it was a little boy I was trying to take home with me tonight?"

"Tee hee...um...I'd be careful that you don't bite off more than you can chew."

We arrive at the Sunoco gas station on Jog and 10th Ave. and before stepping out to buy her beer she says, "You should have a beer with me and by the way honey, I'll chew you up and spit you out!"

"I'm not sure that's a good idea." I reply as she steps out. I'm smiling. *"I can't believe what's going on today. This is crazy. Why am I in these situations? Why do these things keep happening? Why don't I control them better? Why does my lust get the best of me? Help me God."*

She walks back in my car. "THUMP!" "You sure you don't want to have a beer with me? Just have one so I don't drink alone."

"What beer did you buy?"

"I bought Yuengling."

"That is my favorite beer. Really the only one I drink. I tell you what. You're my last ride tonight. Sure. I'll have a beer with you."

"When we get back to my cousin's house I'm going to drop off my luggage and we can go drink by the pool."

"O.K. sounds good. How will we get in?"

"She has a key."

"O.K. cool."

We arrive at her cousins and I open and close her door. "THUMP!" I remove the luggage and wait by the trunk as she rolls them in. I think, *"What am I doing here? I should leave."* She walks out with the pack of beer in her right hand and a key in the other.

"Follow me. It's right over there." She points to a cobbled walkway.

"O.K."

I'm looking around and making sure no one sees us because I'm sure we can't be there during these hours. Once inside the clubhouse area, we sit on the pool chairs and pop open two beers. "PSSSHH."

"Thanks for the beers. Cheers!"

"Cheers. That water sure does look enticing."

"You're crazy. It's cold as hell. Now that jacuzzi sure looks nice."

"Let's go in. I could do the pool. I'm from Michigan. This is perfect weather to me."

"It's a shame I don't have trunks. I'd love to go in that jacuzzi right now with a beer. That would be perfect."

She crosses her legs. "You could skinny dip in there. Go naked. I don't care."

I challenge her. "You first champ."

She cracks a smile, cocks her head diagonally ever so slightly and stares at me for a whole ten seconds in silence. "You silly little boy." She stands up and unzips her dress. She grabs the shoulders straps with her hands and pushes the entire dress down to the floor. In just a G-string, she picks up the remaining beers and moves over to the jacuzzi. I get a rise out of this. Adrenaline and testosterone are pumping. I undress and enter the jacuzzi, sitting close to her but still a respectable distance.

"I only came in here for the beer. Want to pass me one?" I smile.

"I'm sure that's why." She passes me a beer and grabs me with her other hand. She begins to rub me under the water. I open the can of beer and down it within fifteen seconds. With a fist full of her wet hair, I bring her towards my lips. Our kissing gets stronger and stronger when I pull her head back by her hair and gently push her down toward my crotch.

"Oh...Ah...mmm...mmm." When she finished we had another beer.

"Mayi I have to get going. I have to make my flight at 6 A.M. tomorrow."

I look at my watch. "I didn't realize it was midnight already. I have church tomorrow myself. I gotta get going also." We step out of the jacuzzi and air dry rather quickly. I'm still a little damp and throw on my clothes anyways. She throws on her dress.

"Help me zip it please."

I help her zip it up and grab her ass. We walk back towards my car. I give her a hug and a kiss.

"It was nice meeting you. I hope you have a safe flight tomorrow."

"Nice meeting you, too. Thank you for drinking with me tonight."

"Yeah. I had fun. You take care."

I sit in my car damp like unfinished laundry and wet the whole interior. I'm driving home and thought I would feel good. *"I just had these two gorgeous women: a blond and a brunette. So why do I feel so empty? You pig. You huge pig. You hypocrite."*

I've been talking to God almost every day. I talk to him in the car constantly in between customers. I go to church twice a week. My actions this day weigh heavily on my shoulders. *"Why can't I be more Christian like? God knows I want to be. I want to pray but I'm so ashamed. Why would he want to hear from me? Always remorseful after the action. Why can't I remember this feeling before the action? Maybe I let my ego and selfishness take over."*

I just want to forget about today. Funny thing with life. Sometimes it won't let you forget it. Confused, distraught, tired and ashamed I get home and shower. I sit in that shower for a good hour letting the water run down my face hoping it can cleanse me, knowing it can't. I get out, dry off and jump straight into bed trying to hide from the world.

The next morning, I wake up and roll around in bed laying in my shame and guilt. Dragging myself out of bed and walking into the kitchen I search for food in the fridge and cabinets, but I'm so upset I can't eat. Still not sure if God wants to hear from me, I pray.

"Lord thank you for everything you have given me and everything you haven't. Thank you for everyone you have brought in my life and removed. Lord in the name of Jesus Christ I ask that you forgive me for my earthly sins. I ask that you work my heart. Remove this lust from me. Don't give up on me. I'm not giving up on you. Lord, please help me with my feelings towards my wife. I don't know why I let her get under my skin. Give me a sign. Show me. Lord I thank you for my daily bread, whatever it may be I need that day. I thank you for letting me see another wonderful, glorious day. Please open my heart for today's lesson. Again, I love you. I thank you. In the name of Jesus Christ I pray, Amen."

PART II: Gods Playlist

I open my eyes after completing the prayer and realize there is still time to make it to church. Parking at the rear of the packed campus in one of the last spots left I make my way sheepishly to the side entrance of the mega-church and plop down onto the first seat available. The smell of heavy perfume and sweat spreads through the packed rows. The sound of the youth band joyously singing worship songs begins to brighten my spirits and my right foot automatically taps to the hymns.

I've heard the playlist before, but this day, for reasons I'll never know, my ears and heart are wide open when experiencing the first song of the afternoon, "Reckless Love of God." The plucking of the guitar strings inspires me to stand in worship. The boom of the drums and rhythmic piano-playing heighten, and the music bounces from the rafters, enveloping us all in joy. The beats match the pace of my breath and for the first time I realize we are all like those instruments, instruments used to spread the word and love of God.

Here we go with the waterworks. There is a different feeling this time though. It is not shame, guilt, or regrets bringing the tears. It is a feeling of acceptance and purpose creeping up inside me. These songs are talking to me. The instruments aren't all perfect and new, they've seen their dings, wear and tear, but the strings pluck and the flute whistles, playing together, spreading the word.

I finally felt what I searched for since the baptism, when I asked if I should feel different. Since this day God talks to me through song and I gratefully listen. It's the songs that get me, choke me up.

Drums and guitars battle it out to the start of "Open Heaven." I can hardly sing through my tears and cry to the very last lyric. Wiping my eyes, "I Surrender" begins. This song starts with the piano and eventually a violin joins in my cathartic release. The crying hurts in a way that is also liberating, and my prayers are answered. *"God thank you for this moment. I will no longer whine about, or hide, behind my failures. I was wrong to blame You for my hardships. You gave me free will. I chose to act selfish. I chose to ignore right from wrong. No more. No more blaming. I know through all of this You are here to forgive my sins. I know you have forgiven mine and I will not have it be in vain. I need to be kinder to others and myself. You show me there is always hope. I will not squander all you have given me, That's my promise to you, to my son, and to me. Amen."*

I unclasp my hands and bring my head up just as the violin solo reaches its crescendo and to this day that sound is the most blessed sound I have ever heard. My cheeks are soaked, my shirt is wet, and I am warm in the knowledge that God is with me.

Right when I thought I'd be able to get a chance to breath "Touch of Heaven," begins to play. For the first time I really listen and await the violin's arrival after the piano chords run out. God is truly guiding this band of angels. I have a total new outlook on the violin and am determined to learn how to play it.

When the song is over Pastor DS ascends to the stage and begins to speak to the congregation. He starts by welcoming those that have joined online and those in person.

"Good morning Christians!"

"Good morning Pastor DS." The replies come disjointed and quiet from various voices.

"Let me try that again. Good morning Christians!"

"Good morning Pastor DS!" The crowd roars.

"Ah, much better. Today we have a good message. A message about sin. About secret sin. Are you living in secret sin brothers and sisters? It's not so secret, is it? Jesus knows your sin. He knows your sin before and after; yesterday and tomorrow. He died for your sins without you knowing Him. Proverbs 28:13 -For whoever conceals his transgressions will not prosper, but he who confesses and forsakes them will obtain mercy. John 5:17 -All wrongdoing is sin, but there is sin that does not lead to death. Jeremiah 17:9 -The heart is deceitful above all things, and desperately sick, who can understand it. The good news Christians. You don't have to live in secret sin."

My eyes are wide open, ears hollowed out waiting on the Pastor's answer. *"Come on DS. Tell me. Tell me the secret!"*

He continues. "Ecclesiastes 7:20-Surely there is not a righteous man on earth who does good and never sins. You're going to sin brothers and sisters. Confess it to the Lord and repent from the sin. Ask Him to come into your heart when you're thinking of the sin or committing the sin. Don't feel ashamed because you're committing or about to commit it. Go to Him. He wants to help you fight it. Stay away from things that trigger sin. Bad propaganda. Negative music. If you have to hang out less with certain people, do that also. Let's pray."

Pastor DS bows his head and clasps his hands. "Lord I pray that you hear us here tonight. That you would heal and help those going through trials and tribulations. Lord, I pray that you heal their heart tonight. I pray that you touch someone tonight and bring them home to you. Lord we know that no matter what happens today or tomorrow that you are faithful, and your promise is kept. We pray that you forgive us for our sins. In the name of Jesus Christ we pray, and his people said-"

"AMEN!" The crowd erupts.

Pastor DS continues. "If you need prayer, we have Prayer Warriors here. Band will you please play us out?"

I wipe my face quickly and slip out before everyone else leaves. I get in my car and grab my phone, holding it like it's a grenade about to go off. The pastor's words stick with me. I remain seated without turning the car on for several minutes. With conviction I open up my You-Tube and delete all my music playlists. I hit the search button and search for only Christian songs. My playlist starts with eight songs.

The Christian music has a positive effect on my mood from my thoughts to my soul. *"If it does that to me, can it do it to other people? Will it touch other people the way it touches me? Should I try playing this on rides and see what happens?"*

I decide to take the calculated risk and begin playing Christian music while giving rides. People could destroy my driver rating, but I don't care about that. If it could help anyone the way it helped me, it is worth it. I connect my phone to my Android Auto and play these eight songs on repeat. Here is the feedback I received the first day.

Rider 1, "Hey man great music. I needed that."

Ride 2, "I have never gotten in a rideshare and heard Christian music. Keep it up. Great stuff."

Ride 3, "I can tell by the music you're Christian. I love the music."

Ride 4, "I love this song. Play it up please."

The fifth ride is Brittany, and she is this very spunky 5'4 honey-skinned girl. She is wearing greyish pants and a maroon two button shirt tucked in. I peek at my clock and it reads 4:23 P.M. I do my normal spiel. This is a very short ride. I have our very own worship leader, Josh Sherman, conducting a unique rendition of "Psalms23 (I am not alone)," downloaded on YouTube. As the lead vocalist, gospel music runs through his veins. His love and passion erupt when he sings. He leads with sermon and song. Then, the chorus follows with tranquility.

"THE LORD IS MY SHEPHERD. The Lord is my shepherd. HE GOES BEFORE ME. He goes before me. DEFENDER BEHIND ME. Defender behind me. I WONT FEAR. I won't fear. I'M FILLED WITH ANOINTING. I'm filled with anointing. MY CUPS OVERFLOWING. My cups overflowing. NO WEAPON CAN HARM ME. No weapon can harm me. I WON'T FEAR. I won't fear. PEOPLE OF GOD SING HALLELUJAH.

Two minutes away from the drop off I glance back.

"Aww...Sweety what's wrong? Why are you crying?"

She laughs out loud at herself while weeping and wiping away tears with her pointer finger. "Oh no. Don't mind me. My dad is a Pastor and I've never heard this song like this. It's beautiful."

"You're getting a treat today then. This is the worship leader at my church. He's amazing."

"Yes, he is." She continues to wipe tears.

"Yeah, the music gets me, too."

I turn up the volume a bit louder. We arrive at the drop off and I open the door for Brittany. She gets out and asks, "Can I have a hug?"

"Sure." We embrace.

"Thanks for the song. I really enjoyed it and the ride."

"My pleasure mama."

"THUMP!" I get back in my car and start to head back up north. I believe this is the type of music that inspires love and can help unite the world. Still listening as I pull into my parking spot at home, I watch the pinkish sunset evaporate into the ashy night sky. Tears slide down my cheeks in gratitude. I'm compelled to pray.

"God thank you for everything you have given me and everything you haven't. Thank you for everyone you have brought in my life and removed. Lord, thank you for letting me see another glorious day. Lord in the name of Jesus Christ please forgive me for my earthly sins. God, please forgive me for the adultery I believe I have committed. Even though, I'm pretty sure my marriage is over. Show me. Tell me what to do. I'm lost. Don't give up on me. God thank you for the music. The rides were awesome today. Thank you for keeping me busy. In the name of Jesus Christ I pray, Amen!"

By the time I get home, exhausted from the rides and the crying, I don't even change out of my clothes and pass out on top of my comforter.

Through the months of March and April my wife and I text each other a lot. Sometimes good; sometimes bad. We fight, we make up, we have sex. In my mind the intimacy meant we were still connected and perhaps might reconcile. At the same time, I wasn't sure that was a good idea anymore. At this point I was still in love with this woman. Even when texting, I wondered, *"Why love someone who doesn't love me? Why am I torturing myself?"*

Yet the texts continue to fly sporadically back and forth.

"-Besides why would you want to see or be around someone who is malicious? Always doing things to hurt you with intent you claim.-"

"-You think you can talk to me however you want. Like I'm one of your friends. I'm not nor have I ever accepted this because I'm still your wife, not your friend.-"

"-Ditto, you're not my friend and hardly my wife. Have a good day.-"

"-Not your wife anymore, that's for sure.-"

I asked myself, *"Would she ever be content with me? Was this marriage sanctioned by God? All she seems to want is sex and to change me. She said she is not in love with me, and it shows. I will avoid her. She is not healthy for you."*

I ignore her advances for a while.

"-No I don't want to see you right now.-"

"-Why such need to keep avoiding me? You can't keep avoiding me forever. It's so hard for you to just express how you really feel. Why not just say because it hurts too much to see me face to face or something?-"

"-O.K. I'll make the deposit tomorrow.-" I would type back trying to change the subject.

"-I thought you were coming to get your mail.-"

"-Had a full day. Leave it in your porch and I'll come by and get it.-"

Her manipulation was at it's best.

"-Tell me. What do you think would happen if you were to see me? Trust me nothing would happen like it did last time. I don't want to go down that rabbit hole with you again. I can understand if it hurts too much to see me or be near me and not be able to control your emotions because maybe you don't trust yourself with me. I just want you

to know I don't hold any ill feelings or grudge towards you. I do still love you but I know it's time to let go for we are not good for each other.-"

"-Maybe I just don't want to see you. Out of sight, out of mind. I don't hate you. I just don't want to see or be around you. I don't see anything wrong with that. Save the I love you's. I don't believe it.-"

"-Do you think we could ever get to a space where we can be friends. Hate to feel hated by you.-"

There were times when we got along but we remained separated. She never asked me back to the family home and I did not feel right asking to return. The limbo was torture and ruled my days. She texts me and against my better judgement I invite her over.

"-It's a gorgeous moon tonight.-"

"-Yes it is.-"

"-Thinking of you. Miss you.-"

"-Me too.-"

"-Would like to see you.-"

"-O.K. Come over.-"

The scene replays itself over and over throughout the coming weeks. My prayers continued daily asking God to heal our relationship. God does answer, but he gave me what I needed, not what I wanted. The prayer was answered April 30th.

I had just survived my crazy weekend with Suzy. I practiced the Lord's principles of helping the downtrodden with food, clothing and shelter. Listening to Christian music every day in my car forced me to evaluate moments of shame, guilt and fear in my life. Sometimes thinking about my wife, sometimes thinking about the divorce looming.

Hoping for a great day despite this strange new world we are living in, my alarm wakes me at 5 A.M. I turn on my apps and sit back on my couch, inhaling a bowl of cereal while waiting on a ride to come in. "BILILING, BILILING, BILILING!"

My first ride is Ed. He is only half a mile away. Before departure my mental checklist is top priority. *"Alcohol wipes, check. Mask, check. Towel, check."* Feeling blessed to have a job to get up for, COVID-19 hasn't affected me financially. It is slower, but a lot of drivers stopped driving and that has allowed me to thrive. My early morning runs are in demand.

My mask is off, looped around one ear so the customer can see my face matches the profile. I quickly jump out and shout, "I'll get that door so you don't have to touch the handle. You're Ed?"

"Thank you. Yes sir. Mayi?" Ed says hopping in the back seat and putting on his mask.

"Yes sir." I reply and close the door. "THUMP!" I run back, hop in and put on my mask.

Ed is 6'4 and jacked. He's wearing a white button down with three buttons undone at the neck for breathing room.

"Ed we are heading to Chrysler, Dodge in Pompano on Federal Highway?"

"Yes sir. Hey, I hope you don't mind. I'm going to do some work on my laptop on the way down."

"Yeah man. No worries. This is your ride. Do what you gotta do. Temperature O.K?"

"Yes. Thanks."

"You comfortable with seventy five on the highway?"

"Yes sir. Thanks again."

"You're welcome. My pleasure."

Ed types away while Christian music is jamming through my speakers. We are wearing this annoying mask for thirty minutes. I pull my mask down, scratch my itchy noise and put it back on. We don't talk much. When we arrive at Chrysler, Dodge I say, "Ed let me get that door, so you don't have to touch the handle."

"No problem. Thank you, sir. No one is doing that."

I hop out and run to the passenger rear door and open it. Ed pops out.

"Here man. Take this five. You deserve it. The ride was really smooth, and I really enjoyed your music. It's what I needed this morning. It got me going."

"Thanks Ed. Something happened to me a few months ago. That's all I listen to or play in my car now." My list had grown to eighty spiritually uplifting songs.

"Keep it up and thanks for the ride." We give each other a fist pump and Ed walks to Service. No one shakes hands due to Covid. My music has connected me to so many different types of people.

Pulling off to the side of the car dealership to clean, I wipe down the backseats, seatbelts, buckles and handles. Sitting back in the car I lather hand antibacterial gel through each crevice like the media reports say, over and over, counting to twenty. My hands are raw from doing it so much.

Rides bring me up and down the coast. If things keep up, I'll be finishing up early. My next ride comes in with a pick-up request for Kelly from Riviera Beach. Arriving at the blue and green run-down apartment building I spot this skinny, pale white girl with a dirty mask on. Her hair is done up in a messy bun and she is wearing a short black dress better suited for evening hours. Speed walking to the passenger rear door with my mask looping over one ear I verify, "Kelly?"

Kelly jumps back from me. "Shit you scared me jumping out like that. Don't you know where you at?"

"Am I supposed to be scared because I'm in Riviera? I'm sorry for frightening you. I just want to get the door, so you don't have to touch the handle." She enters the backseat.

"Oh. O.K. thank you. You didn't have to do that though."

"Well, if I'm the only one touching the handles no one can spread anything right? I already disinfected back there. Besides, I get to stretch out my legs from being in the car." I put on my mask.

"Oh. I didn't think of that." She mumbles through her mask.

"THUMP!" The door closes, and I round the car to my side, drop in and confirm.

"8436 46th St. Boynton Beach?"

"Yes, hey you think we can make a stop at Wendy's on the way?"

"Yeah. No worries. I got you."

"Thanks. I appreciate that."

I take off. Right before I hop on the I-95 South, I ask, "Temperature O.K.?"

"It's fine. Thank you."

"You comfortable with seventy five on the highway?"

"Yeah, that's cool."

It's not too long of a ride listening to Christian music the whole way from Riviera to Woolbright Road in Boynton Beach. You can see the humidity rising from the highway. My car is clocking ninety degrees. I throw on my glasses to avoid squinting in the bright sun. We arrive at Wendy's at Woolbright Road and Federal Highway. She orders. "Yeah…can I have three- "4 for 4's," two junior bacon cheeseburgers and all cokes for the beverages."

"O.K. that will be $17.96. Please pull up to the next window," responds the drive through attendant. I pull up and hand her my card.

Kelly leans forward and says, "What are you doing? I got it."

"Kelly, I got you. Something told me to get this for you today."

"Well here. Let me give you some money."

"If you give me money, I wouldn't be doing something nice, would I? You would be paying me for what I did. It's on me today."

"Really. Let me give you some money."

"No ma'am. It's cool. I got you."

"Thank you. That's awfully nice of you."

"My pleasure."

We pull out toward the final stop. She leans forward. "Thank you. I really do appreciate it. You just fed my kids today."

"Then it's definitely my pleasure, but don't thank me. Thank God. He has been guiding me."

I pull into the parking lot. "Let me get that door for you so you don't have to touch the handle." I hop out and run around to the other side and open the door.

"Thank you. You are very kind."

"My pleasure. You have a great day and stay safe." She pops out.

"Thank you. You too." I close the door. "THUMP!"

I take a five-minute drive to the beach, a perk of the job. Leaning against the seawall, my eyes span the crowd. Bikinis and tan bodies line the walk. There are more beach goers here than I have seen in a while due to the pandemic. Everyone has grown tired of lockdown. Only a small percentage wear masks.

"BILILING, BILILING, BILILING!" A new ride share has come in. Arriving at the pick-up, Brandy's sleeveless flowery silk top drapes over her jeans. Popping out with my mask looped around one ear and walking to the rear passenger side door, I open it and verify. "Brandy?" Then slide the mask over my face.

"Yes. Mayi?"

"Yes ma'am." She slinks down in the back seat and I close the door. "THUMP!"

"Brandy we are heading to Atlantic Ave. South County Courthouse in Delray?"

"Yes sir." She throws on her mask and says, "I hope you don't mind. I have to make a call," as we pull away and start the ride. She dials her phone.

Replying while lowering the volume, "I don't mind. It's your ride. You do what you got to do."

"Hey sis how are you?...I'm on my way now...No! I'm going to tell the judge he needs to stay in there...I'm sorry you feel that way but I'm tryin' to save his life...If he comes out he will die!...I'm sorry sis...That's too bad...Sorry...If you guys love John and you're honest, you can see his addiction is out of control. I'm going to ask that he stay Baker Acted...Too bad. Look I'm in the middle of a rideshare.

Let me call you when I get out…O.K. love you." She hangs up the phone and looks up at me.

"Hey, I'm sorry about that."

I peek in the mirror. "What are you apologizing about? It's cool. You're good."

"That you had to listen to my family issues. You know, I love my brother, but this is for his own good. He's a bad addict. I hope the judge will listen to what I have to say. Instead of letting him out, he needs to send him to a program. He might get mad at me, but it saved my life when my mother did it to me, God bless her soul."

My wife (or whatever I should call her) calls and I send it to voice-mail. "You can answer that. It's O.K."

"I don't answer the phone when I have customers. It's unprofessional. I want you to know I understand. Listen, you're being a good sister. He might get mad but will thank you once clean and sober." I turn up the volume to "Oceans" by Hillsong United.

"Oh, I love this. I love your music."

"Thank you."

"Anyone ever say you sound like Pit Bull?"

"Actually yes. I hear that all the time. I guess it's my hoarse voice. Dale!" I smile.

She closes her eyes and sings with the music. I join in with my horrible voice. We sing away and the music rises. My voice breaks and scratches trying to hit the high note. Never going to happen. We sing in worship the rest of the ride until we reach the courthouse.

"Thank you for the music. It was great."

"Hey, can I pray for you?"

"That would be nice. Thank you."

I turn and she extends her hand. I grab it with both of my hands and start to pray. "Dear Lord, thank you for letting us see a wonderful, glorious day. Lord I pray that you guide Brandy today. Give her the right words to say and the courage to say them. Open the judge's heart so he understands her trouble and worry for her brother. God, please help her brother break out of this addiction. Help heal him and help him see the other side life has to offer. Lord we know that no matter what happens today or tomorrow that you are faithful, and your promise is kept. Lastly, prepare Brandy's heart to accept whatever the outcome may be today and that it's your plan. We ask that you forgive us for our earthly sins. In the name of Jesus Christ we pray-"

"Amen!"

"Mayi thank you for that. I think you were supposed to drive me today."

"Nothing is a coincidence. Truly believe that. Let me get that door for you."

I turn and hop out. Make my way and open the door. "Good luck in there. God be with you."

She steps out. "Thank you. May God keep you safe while you drive."

"Thank you." I close the door. "THUMP!" I begin to drive home and hold back tears. *"Can God really use me? But I'm so broken myself. How can I be of any use to him? I can't get my life together. How am I going to help others with theirs? I'm such a hypocrite."*

I call my wife back. "Hey. What's up?"

"Are you home?"

"No but I can be in twenty minutes. You want to come over?"

"Yes."

I arrive at my apartment and shower. I throw on a pair of boxers and make myself a ham and cheese sandwich. She arrives. "KNOCK... KNOCK...KNOCK!"

I shout. "Come in. It's open." She walks in and sits on the grey couch.

"You look good as usual. You do that on purpose." I say and she smiles and giggles while pulling on her sports bra.

"It doesn't matter what I wear. You always find me irresistible."

I smile. "I can't help it. Anyways, today was crazy. I prayed with someone. It was awesome. I'm going to keep playing Christian music.

I'm not going to talk about it unless someone insists but I'm going to keep playing the music. Maybe it will help someone."

She gets closer, touches me and bites her bottom lip. "You know you're my weakness. You turn me on so much."

"And you're mine but you know, how long are we going to keep sneaking around like this? Huh, sneak! Yeah, I'm going to call you Sneaky."

We laugh and she says, "Oh shut up. It's no one's business and we are married."

"True, True."

I really didn't want to have sex with her that day. We needed to talk. We had sex, but it felt different. She wasn't emotionally invested.

We don't talk again until four days later. The whole weekend was really tough on me, spent sulking around the apartment. This Monday was the day I was going to come clean to my wife, face whatever the consequences were for my actions. I was going to ask her to reconcile.

Part III: Ask and Receive

I wake up at 6 A.M. and prepare myself for the day. The unemployment rate has inflated to 13% due to COVID-19 and a national lockdown is still in progress. I thank God that I still have been able to work and ask him for courage. I turn on my apps and immediately my first ride comes in. "BILILING, BILILING, BILILING!"

My pickup is for Jeremiah at the Wawa on Lake Worth Road and Congress Ave. I arrive at the Wawa and there's a balding black man, wearing all black from head to toe, seated at a table. He's the only person there so I park in front of him, hop out, jog to the rear passenger door holding my mask that's looped on one ear and open it with the other. "Jeremiah?"

"Yes. Mayi?" He stands up from the table.

"Yes sir. That's me."

"I'm sorry. It said you were still on your way."

"Yeah, you can't pay attention to that all the time." He gets in the car and I close the door. "THUMP!" I get in, put on my mask and confirm, "836 Silver Beach Road, Riviera Beach?

"Yes sir." I turn the volume up on the Christian music, hop on the highway and go through my normal spiel.

Jeremiah compliments me halfway through the ride. "You're a pretty good driver. I like the way you get through traffic. I like the way you bob and weave."

"Thank you, Jeremiah. I have been driving here since I was fifteen years old. Hey, temperature O.K.?"

"Yes, sir it is."

"Everything O.K. today? You seemed a little flustered when I picked you up."

"I'm gonna be honest. I was already home where you're taking me now. I was pissed because I forgot to leave the key. So now you're taking me back home. Your music though. It's what I needed this morning. It has calmed me down. I've never seen or heard a man playing Christian music for another man."

"Well that's all I play in my car now so a lot of men will hear it in here."

"You keep playing that. I dig it."

"Thank you. I appreciate that."

Before arriving at the drop off another call enters my queue. It's not too far in Riviera but deeper into the bad area. Once at the drop off, I pop out and open Jeremiah's door.

He gets out. "Thank you, my man. That was a great ride. God bless you."

"Jeremiah, you take care and be safe my brother." I close the door. "THUMP!"

I added seven really good hip-hop Christian songs. "Home" by Tedashi is playing. Parking on the side of Publix, I wipe down the back seats and seat belts, making sure not to miss the buckles. Pulling back to the front entrance a man with dreads waves at me and I confirm out my window, "Shawn?"

"That's me. Mayi?"

"Yes sir. Do you want help with your groceries?"

"Could you please?"

"Yeah, no problem." I put on my mask and help him load the groceries.

Once loaded, I open the passenger rear door and Shawn sits in. "You think we could stop by McDonald's on the way?"

"Yeah Shawn. No worries."

"Yo, G. What's this bad ass hip hop you got going on? Never heard this bad ass beat."

"Would you believe me if I told you this is Christian music?"

"Nah man. For reals?"

"Yeah bro. Listen to what he's saying. It's pretty deep. It matches those beats you like. After this I got another good one for you."

Shawn leans forward. "Yo, G. That's bad for reals!"

"I know. I didn't know it could be this good."

I arrive at McDonald's and roll down his window.

"Welcome to McDonald's. What would you like to order?"

"Yes…Ummm, can I get a Sausage McMuffin with egg, a hash brown and a small coffee?"

"Yes sir. That will be $5.17. Please drive up to the second window."

We drive up and I hand them my card.

"Yo, what you doing G?"

"I got you today bro. It's on me."

"You sure man? Let me give you some money."

"Then it wouldn't be on me would it?"

"Yo, G. I appreciate that."

"My pleasure." The attendant hands me his food and I pass it back.

Shawn repeats himself. "For reals G. Thank you dog."

"You're welcome man." I put up a fist pound and Shawn pounds it and sits back with his food. Shawn is eating his breakfast when we arrive at the drop off on PGA and Military Trail.

"I'll help you with the groceries. I can take them to the doorstep."

"Thanks G. Appreciate that. No rideshare has ever helped with the groceries."

"I hear that a lot because I always offer to help. Especially with this COVID-19. I always ask first. I don't know if you want me touching your stuff, but I have hand sanitizer with me." I help Shawn with his groceries and when I lay the last bag down, he extends his hand.

"Yo, take this man. Thank you for breakfast G." He tries to hand me a $5 bill.

"Thanks bro. I appreciate it but it's on me today."

"For reals. Thanks, my G."

"Shawn you stay safe."

As we part ways, the "Money Maker" comes in. My phone flashes, "45 mins. plus," and I immediately accept the call. I wipe the back down, put hand sanitizer on my hands and roll out to Carl. Arriving at the pin, the countdown begins as I reach out to Carl.

"Hello Carl? I'm here but I don't see you."

"You're in the wrong place."

"I'm where the pin says to be, but it could be wrong. Tell me where you are so I can pick you up?"

"I'm outside and I don't see you. I bet you're at the wrong address. You stupid kids only know how to follow the stupid GPS. The address is right, and I bet you're at the wrong place."

"Well Carl I'm at the pin. I can only go where the GPS tells me to go. I'm from the area and pretty good with directions. Tell me where you are, and I'll come get you."

"Try going around the corner. I bet it took you to the street on the other side."

"O.K, Carl. I'll be right there."

There is an old man in his 70's tapping his foot impatiently on the curb when I round the bend. Sweat is pouring down his yellow-collar shirt and there is a coffee-stain on his khakis. I have my mask looped around one ear, jump out, and open the door.

"It's about damn time!" Carl yells.

"Yes sir." I close the door. "THUMP!" Strap on my mask and run to my side and verify the address. "515 Coral Ridge Dr, Coral Springs?"

"Yes. My doctor is out there. I lived out there before."

"Do you want me to take the Turnpike? That's the way it's telling me to go."

"Yes. I think that's the fastest way. Do you know how to get there? Will we make my 11:45 A.M. appointment?"

This is going to be my last drive of the morning, having surpassed my money goal for the day. "I think it's the fastest way also and we will make your appointment. I just wanted to ask if you wanted me to take the Turnpike because I pay the tolls now, but they charge you for them and repay me immediately. I know most of the way. I have lived here all my life, but don't know Coral Ridge that well. I have the GPS."

"See you stupid little kids don't know crap. You have to rely on that GPS computer. You don't know anything or even how to get to my house."

"Carl, I don't think I'm that stupid. You gave me simple directions and I followed them and found you, right?" I merge on the Ronald Reagan Turnpike south, off of PGA Blvd.

"Yes, but you were still lost. Back in my day we had to use maps to find our way. You kids are spoiled."

"Yes, and it won't be the last time, but I found you right away. I drove when maps were used also. Anyways, if it makes you feel better we are going to take the Turnpike to the Sawgrass West and get off at Coral Ridge. From the looks of the GPS, we will briefly head North to our location. Temperature O.K.?"

"Yes. Thanks."

"You comfortable with seventy five on the highway?"

"Yes, that's fine. Just get me there in one piece."

"Will do." I raise the volume on the Christian music trying to taper his anger.

Passing Delray entering Boca I hear some loud tapping in the back. I slightly pivot to my right and peek out of the corner of my eye. Carl is tapping his right index finger to the beat against the inner door handle. I'm smiling inside. Then he says, "So where you from?"

"I was born in Cuba but funny you ask now because I was raised here in Boca. We are driving through it right now."

"So, you and your family were able to get out?"

"Carl, we got out in 1980. I have been here forty years. Grew up twenty years in Boca. Great city."

Carl leans forward. "That's good. I'm happy you were able to get out."

"Thanks Carl. I appreciate that. So, you like the music?"

"I love Christian music. Never heard it in a rideshare before."

"Well then you're in for a treat." He lounges back in his seat.

We don't talk the rest of the ride until reaching Coral Ridge Drive.

"Mayi make a left at the next light."

"Got it boss."

"Now it's the building right in front."

"Got it." I park next to the curve. "Let me get that door for you Carl."

It takes him a minute because he is weaker at this age. Finally, out of the car he says, "Great ride young man. I'm sorry about earlier. You handled yourself well."

"No worries Carl. Sometimes you just have to let people cool off and understand from their perspective. I could understand it's probably happened before, and the frustration just built up. It's cool man."

He reaches in his pocket and pulls out a $10 bill and hands it to me. "Thanks again."

I accept the tip. "Thank you, my friend. Anytime." I close the door. "THUMP!" I stroll back to my door and get in. My wife will be off for lunch in seventeen minutes, so I head over to the gas station to use the rest rooms and to fill my tank. While waiting for my wife's break, I try to pump myself up and ready for the conversation. *"O.K. gotta suck it up. Gotta be a man and tell her. Tell her you love her. You want to come home."* I wait nine minutes past the hour and call. The honking of horns is drowned out by my A/C blasting. The phone begins to ring through the car speakers, and I consider hanging up. Instead I wipe the sweat from my brow and blurt out, "Hey how are you?"

"I'm O.K. and you?"

"I'm doing alright. I was wondering if we could talk?"

"Mayi I wanted to talk about the other day."

"Good. Me, too. Go ahead. Go first."

"Mayi…It felt different. I didn't enjoy it as much. I didn't want to do it. I think you felt it, too."

"I did. It was like you weren't there. You were somewhere else."

"I think this is the closure I needed. We needed. Don't you agree?"

"Uh...closure…yeah…sure I guess."

"Yeah, I just wasn't feeling it. Did you have something you wanted to say?"

"No. That was it. That was pretty much it."

"I'm sorry. I know you still hurt at times badly."

"It's O.K. I'll be O.K. Well, that's that."

"Mayi, I hope we can still be friends."

"I doubt right now. Maybe, but I'm not sure. I gotta go. Gotta get back to work."

"Have a great day Mayi."

"Yeah. You, too."

Just like that it was over, and I didn't say anything. When she spoke it felt final and I thought, *"Why cause any unnecessary hurt? This must be the sign I have been praying for. Not what I was expecting Lord, but for the best."*

From April 30th through Father's Day, I cried a lot. The music and the customers were my healing. We talked about my divorce and their issues. My wife still randomly texted me here and there. At one point requesting to meet at Kia for her car repair. Another time she asked me to go to the courthouse. Other than that, her communications where short and cold, but always claiming she wanted to be friends. Both appointments are declined the same way.

"-Nah. I think you should go alone without me.-"

"-Ugh, You're such a sellout Mayi!-"

"-I'm sorry. I just don't want to or am ready to see you-."

"-O.K. I understand.-"

Father's Day arrives and I plan on spending it with my mom and dad. It's not my weekend with my son so it feels bittersweet.

"Dad, where's mom?"

"I don't know Papo. I think she's working."

"Oh, I find it weird she is not here."

"No Mayi. She works all day on Sundays now taking care of an elderly couple."

"O.K dad. Just wondered."

My sister is in the kitchen mashing potatoes. Hugging my sister from behind when she's not looking, "You know, no matter what, I love you sis."

She tears up and turns red. "I love you, too, big bro." We give each other a huge embrace. About an hour later the doorbell rings. "DING DONG...DING DONG...DING DONG!"

"Hey, you guys expecting company?" I ask.

"Nope." My sister answers.

I open the door. My son and his mom are standing at the threshold. My son wraps his arms around me. "Hi Papo. I love you. I miss you. How are you?"

"I'm great Papi. I missed you too." He darts into my sisters' room and his mom walks in behind him.

I give her a kiss on the cheek. "Hey, how are you?"

"I'm O.K."

"Well, you should stay and eat with us."

"You sure? If it's ok with you guys."

"Of course, it is. My Dad is going to make you anyways."

We sit around the table enjoying steak with rice and beans, mashed potatoes and Cuban bread with butter but the holiday feels somber. This is the first year my mom has not been around for Father's Day and it had nothing to do with COVID-19. While the government mandated no gatherings of ten or more, it had been quite a while since my immediate family of five had been in the same room.

By the end of July, COVID-19 is running ramped. It's a usual bipolar South Florida day. Scattered rains here and there. Start, stop, start again and stop. I'm in an unsafe area of Miami Gardens. It's drizzling and I don't like to drive in the rain, especially in Miami. I ask God, *"Why do you have me here? Why am I in this ghetto? This place is dangerous."*

I reach the pick-up and a little Haitian lady with a huge cooler is waiting outside under an overhang. I throw on my mask and I dart out in the rain, open the door and confirm, "Simone?"

"Yes."

"Do you need help with your cooler?"

"Please, sure please."

She hurries in the car to get out of the rain. I close the door. "THUMP!" I'm playing in the rain loading her big blue cooler.

I confirm the address. "637 Stirling Road, Hollywood."

"Yes sir."

"Awesome. You're bringing me back up north a little. Simone, I think you're going to be my last ride this morning. Temperature O.K?"

"Yes. Thank you, sir." Accelerating slowly because roads are slick from hot temperatures and rain, I maneuver around poorly filled potholes. I approach I-95 on Ives Dairy Road and jump on the North on ramp.

"You comfortable with seventy five on the highway?"

Choking up she says, "Yes. Waaa…waaa…waaa." She cannot control her crying.

"Simone what's wrong? Are you O.K.?" I ask looking in the mirror.

"I'm sorry it's just…waaa…waaa…waaa. My sister passed a year ago today." The crying continues profusely in my car.

"Simone mama I'm so sorry to hear that. I wish there was something I could do to help." She continues crying. I turn up the Christian music to try to soothe her. This ride normally takes twenty minutes but with the construction, storm and traffic it's up to thirty-seven minutes long. Minutes before arrival, I'm asking God to give me the words for her. My eyes start to tear up, I'm trying to hold them back, but I'm feeling her pain.

When we reach her stop, she says, "I'm sorry. I didn't mean to cry the whole way."

I turn to her with tears running down my face, eyes red and puffy, "I'm sorry. I couldn't help but cry listening to your hurt. May I pray for you?"

"Please." She extends her hand out towards me and I hold it with both of mine. I'm taking a risk that this is what God wants. It is rare to feel human touch outside of family now. People are too afraid to catch COVID-19 and even a handshake could be a death sentence.

"Dear God, Lord in Heaven, please listen to us today. We thank you for letting us see another wonderful, glorious day. For no day is promised and each day is a gift. Lord we thank you for everyone you have brought in and out of our lives." Simone starts to cry a little heavier. Trying not to choke up, I continue. "With that being said Lord, I know Simone is hurting right now. She's hurting pretty bad. Help her understand that you have a plan. It may not be the plan we want or that we understand but that everything is on your time. I'm sure her sister is there in Heaven with you, and you may have needed her in your call to fight. Give her the faith to keep moving forward Lord, to keep pushing on. Some days will be harder than others but allow her to seek you in times of need. I know she is a good woman and needs your help. Heal her heart. Lord we love you. We thank you. We pray that you forgive us for our earthly sins. In the name of Jesus Christ we pray, Amen!"

Simone opens her eyes and touchingly asks, "Are you a pastor?"

With tears flowing out I chuckle. "No. I am a devoted Christian who Jesus Christ has saved a number of times."

"I don't know how you do it. Life is hard. I try. I try to believe and go to church and be good. Sometimes I'm just not sure."

"Simone that's the enemy. He wants you to feel shame and guilt. He wants you to feel unworthy, so you stay away from God. Mama don't get it twisted. I have my demons and issues I'm dealing with. Life is hard for me, too, but differently. I'm going through a tough divorce. I love all women a bit too much. My son is struggling in school. I feel like I'm failing him. His mother is a mess. I feel like I'm falling apart, but I always hold on to Jesus. Him and my son keep me going. I have to keep moving. You need to keep moving. Find something to hold onto. Your sister wants you to live."

"Are you sure you're not a pastor?"

I smile and get a laugh again. "I'm sure. Let me open the door for you, so you don't have to touch the handle." I run trying not to get soaked, pop the trunk, remove her cooler and place it on the ground.

Opening her door, she grabs my hand and reaches for a hug saying, "Thank you for your encouragement."

"Simone keep moving forward. Keep fighting. God loves you. I would love to stay and talk but I'm getting wet." I close her door. "THUMP!" I run back over to my door and we wave goodbye. Believing my actions with Simone were the purpose of my day, I turn the apps off and ride home with a feeling of peace. To make my morning even sweeter an unexpected call chimes in.

"RING, RING, RING!" I look at my phone and think, *What is she doing calling me? Wonder what's up with her?"*

Answering the phone, the female voice on the other side laughs, "Hello. Do you remember me? Do you know who this is?"

"Of course, I do. I got you locked in. I've been wondering what ever happened to you. How are you Suzy?"

"I had to call you. I'm back here on the east coast of Florida. My mom is picking me up from the Ft. Lauderdale airport and taking me to a half-way house in Clearwater. I'm clean and sober and I want to thank you. You saved my life that weekend."

"I'm not so sure. I let you smoke that dope."

"Dude you gave me exactly what I needed. You let me be myself without judging me. You gave a total stranger your trust and brought a crack head in your home who could have been a thief. Most would steal in order to pay for their high. You showed me your prize possession, the Tom Brady rookie card. You trusted me when no one else did. I won't forget about that. You could have just left me somewhere unsafe. You were a total gentleman. You brought me back to God. I am forever grateful."

"Let's give the credit to Jesus. I was just his tool that day. In His name. In His glory. I'm so excited to hear from you and that you're clean. That's awesome."

"When I'm done with this halfway house and get back over there let's do a coffee."

"Sounds good mama. I'm proud of you. Keep working hard. I'm working on something myself. I'll let you know when the time is right." I had started writing a book and no one knew yet. Instead of sulking, God had given me a knew passion, writing.

"Keep in touch."

"O.K bye Suzy."

Staring up through the windshield at the sky silently for three minutes processing the call, the sobbing and wretching begins. "Waaa… waa…waa…eh…eh!" Look in the visor mirror you can tell I have been "ugly crying," making noises I've heard only a few times in my life. I yell out to the Heavens, "Are you serious God? Are you serious right now? You can really use me? There's no way. What is going on here?" Pulling myself together, my first call is to Edward England, my church confidant throughout my marriage and impending divorce. He picks up right away.

"Ed you got a few minutes?"

"For you my friend I have more than a few minutes. What's up?"

"Ed you're never going to believe this but I'm praying with people in my car. I think the music is helping people. It could just be me, but I'm going to keep using the platform and doing what I'm doing. It's been crazy Ed."

"Mayi, I think what you're doing is awesome. Do what the Lord calls you to do."

"Ed, I had to call and tell someone. Thanks for listening sir. I'll swing by soon."

"O.K. brother. You have a great day. Come by anytime. You're always welcome."

"Have a great day as well my friend and thank you for everything. Bye."

We hang up and I arrive at home, feeling super motivated to write. So inspired by today's events, the words flowed off my fingers onto my laptop. Don't eat. Don't shower. Don't answer any calls. Just write. I write from 1 P.M. to 3 A.M. and would have kept going but needed sleep for the next workday.

From July through August my contact with my wife continues to be limited. She is colder and shorter. I don't really care to communicate with her. She's on my ass about getting the divorce. I send her a few songs hoping to have our interactions softened. The music has no effect on her. While she remains cold to me, she has no problem asking for favors typically reserved for a significant other.

She requests that I babysit the dog at the townhome for a weekend. It is awkward while sitting on the couch that is not mine anymore, inside a home that is not mine anymore, watching a dog that is not mine anymore either. In fact, this place never felt like home. Imagine my surprise when I received a call from a friend a few days later at my apartment.

"Hey Mayi. How are you?"

"I'm ok. You know going through this divorce, but I'm O.K. I just have to remember the reasons I'm not there but it's hard at times."

"Let me ask you something. Did you know she has a boyfriend and has had one for some time now?"

"What? What are you talking about? Are you serious? Are you sure?"

"Would I lie to you? You know where my loyalty stands. I have nothing to gain."

I get up off the couch, walk outside and start circling the building like a cat on the prowl. It stings. It hurts. I continue on the phone. "Do you know she had me over there twice in the last month to take care of her dog? Continues to let me say intimate things to her. I've done my crap, but I'm not stupid enough to start another relationship this quickly."

"I'm letting you know so you don't get played."

"I appreciate it. Good looking out."

"Yeah. I just see you in a slump and I think it's time you came out. Maybe you needed to know this."

"You could be right. Thanks again."

"Anytime Mayi. You know I love you."

"Talk to you soon. Thank you."

I'm shaking and pace so much around my complex that my old baseball injury is aggravated. By the time I come down my knees are the size of tennis balls. I text her.

"-WOW! You move quick. Enjoy your boyfriend but you are never to use my family and I again. Descarada! You have the audacity to have me over and gave me a hard time about you and Oakley deserving my loyalty. This proves to me you married me for security, and you need a man for financial security. You used me. Lose my number and never call or text me for anything again. Couldn't even wait for

the divorce but that is your M.O. isn't it? That's why none of your relationships are sanctioned by God. You enter them still being married. It's what you did with me and it's what you're doing now. I hope you have a long honey moon stage.-"

Tossing and turning all night, our five years together plays out. The sneaking around is what bothered me. She saw no issue with manipulating me. Maybe it wasn't friendship she was after. Maybe she wanted someone to do her bidding. Still moping while getting ready for work, a text comes in.

"-You don't deserve an explanation but feel you need closure for this chapter in your life. He was introduced to me April 25. The day you were with Suzy. We met a month later in person. I feel my life is not your business anymore. Let me remind you I wasn't divorced when I met you also. Who are you to judge me? Please don't ever text me or contact me again. I hope you can move on and find happiness. I wish you the best.-"

I email her back.

"-You have some nerve. We had sex April 30 and it was different. Of course, it was. You had already met the new boyfriend and came to my apartment to make a decision and you made it on one bad sexual experience. You're disgusting. What hurts me more is that you had so many chances to tell me and I had to find out how I did. You didn't even have the balls or maybe you were just too busy pulling the strings. I'm glad I sold out at the last moments for Kia and Court. I knew something was up. You should have called your freaking boyfriend. Not me Puta! I hope this works out for you, but I doubt God will sanction this one also. Sending you an email because I am blocking all other communications with you. Since it's not my business anymore I will be looking out for my interest and not yours since it's obvious you're only looking out for yours. I wish you the best with your new man. Have a nice life.-"

My anxiety is wound tighter than the shoelaces on my Nikes. I'm not hungry and haven't eaten. Exiting the apartment for work, my hands tremble lightly while pushing the "START" button. Backing out is difficult while yelling, "I WANT THIS OVER!"

Before my first ride share my phone alerts me to a new email. *"-Why are you doing this? Why are you being an ass? I know you probably don't care but I'm having surgery soon. I might not make it. Five years with you have finally caught up to me.-"*

My reply is simple. *"-Your words not mine. Your life is no longer my concern. I don't owe you an explanation. Just like you don't owe me anything, remember? Whatever you have going on, you said is none of my business. Still blaming me for everything. I wish you the best.-"*

The rest of the week I cry, pray, and fall to my knees many times, asking God, "Help me with my aching heart. I know you have gotten me through this before and will do it again. I have faith in you to get me through this. Amen."

I break down in front of friends, including PJ.

"Don't come here with that crying crap." PJ demands.

"Sorry bro." I reply, sitting on the couch petting his Rottweiler, "I don't even come here for you bro. I come for Pippin. Your dog is the sweetest to me. My eyes are like waterfalls. I can't control it. I'll leave."

"What are you talking about dog? You just got here."

Wiping my eyes, "Yeah, but look at me bro. I can't stop fucking crying."

PJ sits across from me on the couch, flipping through channels on his flat screen, refusing to look at me in my dramatic state, "Dog you gotta let go of that ego and selfishness. You know you guys weren't going to get back together. If she weren't with anyone, you wouldn't be like this. I never even liked her. You should be happy you escaped from her. She is a piece 'a work!"

"Bro, I get that." Tears running down my face. "I have no right feeling how I feel. But it hurts bro. I thought I'd be prepared for this. She got me good. Stings."

"I know man. I went through this with my ex. You need to concentrate on things like our championship game this Sunday. Your book that your writing sounds like healthy time spent. Wanna' go hit some balls?"

"Nah. Not in the mood. Have you walked Pippin?"

"Not yet."

"I'm gonna walk him and then go home."

"Dale!"

Dogs truly relieve my stress and offer unconditional love. On the walk Pippin marks up the grass, garage door, and a trash can. By the time we return, its dusk.

"Yo PJ, I'll come back later in the week." Try to have a better second half of the week, kid."

"I'll try." We give each other dap and I take off, still an emotional mess, going over the good and bad days of the marriage. Writing helps. I have motivation burning through my bones, staying up into the early morning hours often. Whatever it takes to distract me from the pain.

Staying up late all week writing, I skip breakfast, and barely eat a meal a day. A month-old laundry pile almost reaches the ceiling and the dishes in the sink are piled up, smelling like old bleu cheese. Paperwork and bills are scattered on chairs and the table.

Forcing myself to work, I take a long, hot shower and finally shave my unruly salt-and-pepper beard. Gel slides into my hair, soaking in immediately, after going unused for weeks. I turn my apps on, walk out to my car, and check the back seats and rugs for cleanliness. The back seat has a sticky situation. Walking back to my apartment to grab wipes to disinfect the back seat, a ride share pings.

"BILILING, BILILING, BILILING!" Debby is less than a mile away at JFK hospital. Not a place to go during this scary time. Hospitals are mainly being used to isolate COVID-19 patients. I nervously pull up to the empty valet area of the hospital within three minutes of the alert. No valet in sight, only a hastily written sign stating,

"Closed until Further Notice." Another COVID-19 casualty. Debby and her nurse are positioned in the center of the sidewalk at the slope ready to move her wheelchair out of ground zero. Both are wearing disposable masks and frustration on their faces.

I put on my mask, dart out and open the rear passenger door. The nurse is struggling with Debby, who weighs at least 250 pounds. She finally pushes her into position in the backseat and snaps her seatbelt. She disappears before another word can be said, running back at top-speed through the double doors of the hospital. "THUMP!" I close the back door and lock in my own seatbelt once seated, and confirm, "596 Brandy Street, Lantana?"

"Yeah, it's a little drive."

"Lucky for you Debby, I do big rides and small rides." She laughs. I turn up the music a little.

Debby asks, "So how long you been a Christian?"

"For quite a few years now Debby and you?"

"Well, gosh, I'd say over ten years."

"Nice." I say as I glance in the mirror.

I make a right into her driveway and she asks, "Can I make a prayer request?"

"Absolutely! What is your request?"

"I need us to pray for God to send me the right person for a position I'm trying to fill. I need a bookkeeper."

She extends her hand forward and I grab it with both of mine.

"God has time for all of us. No matter how big or small the request. No matter how long or short the ride." I say, winking at her.

We begin to pray. "Lord, help Debby. Bring her the right person for the position. Lord guide her in her decision making to recognize your will. We love you. We thank you and we know that you are worthy. In the name of Jesus Christ please forgive us for our earthly sins. In the name of Jesus Christ we pray, Amen."

"Thank you Mayi. That was sweet of you."

"Give me a moment and let me get the door for you." I dash over to her door and open it.

"I'm going to need your help. My feet don't work too well."

"Give me your key. Let me open the door. You wait and hold on to this here." Sometimes my job as a driver expands into medical care.

She hands me the keys and holds on to my door edge. I walk up to her front stoop and twist the key in the lock. While pushing on the handle, I hear behind me, "AH…ah..ah…oh..oh…oh no!"

Debby is on the other side of my car splayed out on the ground. She can only sit up at her waist. Her purple, swollen feet are of no use. The things we do. Risking COVID-19 infection yet again, my only option is to bear hug this stranger and force her up as quick as possible.

"O.K. Debby the only way this is going to work is by us hugging each other. Any other way will hurt my back. I have to get close enough to lift with my legs."

"O.K. come on."

We struggle, successfully placing her in the wheelchair on the fourth try. Both of us are tired and sweaty.

"Thank you Mayi. I wish I had money to tip you."

"Don't worry about it, Debby. You take care and be safe." I spring back in my car. Rides usually chime in about every ten minutes or less. Lately, rides are not popping up as often. Twenty minutes pass before my next call. COVID-19 is killing people and businesses. I drive two beautiful blondes in a row who speak of depression and suicide attempts.

Blonde #2 declares a minute into the ride, "Your music is so ironic considering the times we are in. Makes me wonder. You must really believe. Huh. Interesting."

I look in the mirror and she has tears running down her face. "Is the music making you depressed? I can turn it off."

She wipes her cheeks. "On the contrary. The lyrics give me hope. I'm on furlough with the airlines. Still getting paid. My boyfriend left me after lockdown began. Didn't want to quarantine with me, he said. After two years together! Been completely alone for months. The depression hit an all-time low the other day and I ate twenty-four pills."

My voice takes a stern tone. "Mama! You can't be eating pills like that. I just picked you up from the beach. You are still getting paid when a lot of people are not. You essentially are getting paid to hang out at the beach. You can't let a man or loneliness take you to that low." I scratch my forehead. "This pandemic won't last forever. You are a beautiful woman and plenty of guys out there will be chasing you once this lockdown is over. Get through the loneliness. Not to be a bible thumper but if you turn to Jesus, you will never be lonely."

Her home is right down the street from the beach, she could've walked. Upon exiting the car, she asks, "Can I have a hug…PLEASE?"

I smile, "Sure." After shutting her door, we embrace and I whisper to her, "Keep your head up. Keep it moving."

We release our grasp and she says, "Thank you for your kind words. You are very sweet."

Making eye contact to try to get through to her I reply, "Keep it moving and pray. Always pray. He will answer."

I get back in the car, not wanting her to get the wrong impression. Since playing Christian music women (and men) had stopped hitting on me. Another blessing.

A call comes in requesting a pick-up down the street for Peter. I stop at the Wawa on the way and do my COVID-19 wipe-down of the car. I throw on my mask, spring out and rush to the rear passenger side door, open and confirm. "Peter?"

"Yes, Mayi?"

"Yes sir." Peter ducks in the back and I close the door. "THUMP!"

"Peter we are heading to 665 Edge Road?"

"That's correct."

"Temperature O.K.?"

"Yes." I play up the Christian music. It's going to be a short two-mile ride. About halfway Peter says, "It's funny you're playing this music. You Christian?"

"Yes, sir, and you?"

"I am. I have been to Faith Farms twice. You heard of it?"

"I have. It's on 441 right?"

"Yes." We pull into Peter's driveway and park my car. Peter points at a white, newer model sports car in the driveway, "You see that BMW? I haven't moved it. I'm scared to drive because I'm scared I'll drink. I'm a recovering alcoholic. I have been clean and sober sixteen years until two days ago. I put my girlfriend through hell." Peter starts to cry. "She said I gave her so much anxiety from my relapse that she had to go to the hospital yesterday. I ruined an amazing relationship. I couldn't visit her because of COVID-19. She doesn't even want to see me again. She is staying with an ex-boyfriend."

I turn around. "Man, Peter, I'm sorry to hear that." Starting to tear up, "I'm actually going through a divorce. Got some shitty news myself last week. I don't mind her moving on. I'm really upset how I feel she kept me there for the things she needed while having a boyfriend. She should have just gone to him. I have been crying for a few days. I think it's just my ego."

Peter wipes his eyes, runs his hand down to his chin and presses against his eyes again. "Should I tell you this?" He pauses, "Yes I should. We are being honest with each other. This might be good to tell you. It eats at me. I had it all man. Then when I was nineteen, I lost everything. My girlfriend at the time was riding in my Jeep. I was drinking and driving and rolled the Jeep over. She was thrown out of the Jeep and back in through the windshield. I got thrown out, but my foot got twisted in the bolts of the door hinge. I rolled seven times with the Jeep."

"Peter, man! You're lucky to even be here."

"I wish I was the one dead and not her. It eats at me every night. The cops said the same thing. Blah, blah…I'm lucky. Lucky and haunted."

I ask, "That's when the heavy drinking started, right?"

"Yeah. I was never able to control it after that without help. Taking someone's life that you loved is the most difficult thing. I have done two stints at Faith."

"I can see how that is traumatizing. Like going through death over and over. God must have saved you for a reason."

Peter's tears trigger me to cry. Here are two grown men, strangers, crying about their relationships and pouring out their grief. We sat in his driveway for forty-five minutes talking and crying. I grab a piece of loose paper, one of the bills I've been ignoring, and write my number below the past due notice. I jump out and open his door. I hand him the paper and say, "If you ever need to talk, cry, chill, just give me a call. If I don't pick up right away it's because I have a customer and will call you back."

"Cool man. I'll do that." We give each other a fist pound and he heads toward his front door with his head down, not looking back, walking, literally through life, just trying to put one step in front of the other. I close the door. "THUMP!" I enter my side, deciding to call it for the day and go home to write.

I get home at noon and cast my phone to my TV, hitting play on "I Surrender." I open the laptop, placing it on the couch armrest. The wounds that are still fresh, especially after speaking with Peter, take over my better judgment. I find myself scrolling through the text history over the past few months, thinking, *"How could she? I can't believe her. How dare she?"* Feeling played like a puppet, rage stirs inside me. Then I go back in the texts another three months, and another before reaching total melt down. My anger turns into sorrow. Throwing my laptop on the ground, I yell, "Fuck!" spiral around and with a misguided force, punch the wall. "OUCH!"

"Forgot that was made of concrete." Wounded, I lay on the bed and whimper in pain and loss, for my swollen hand and broken heart. I force myself to pick the laptop back up, sit down, and write the chapter in the book I have been dreading, the chapter about the pending divorce and think, *"This is all my fault. Oh my God I was so nasty. How could I have said those things? I loved her so much. What's wrong with me?"*

I grieve out loud, "Please God I am so sor...sor...sorrrry. This is ma...my fault. Please forgive me Lord." Hardly able to get the words out, "Waa...waa...waaa." I begin pacing inside my apartment. My cheeks are soaked, my knees are swollen. I get up and grab my phone off the couch and call PJ, but he doesn't pick up. I text him.

"-Yo this part is killing me bro. I can't stop crying dude. This book, this chapter has given me a lot of self-revelation. This is my fault bro. I caused this. This is my fault.-"

"-Yeah, it is! All of it! I was waiting for you to get to this part. This book isn't what you thought it was going to be. I saw it turning, waiting for you to see it. You thought you were writing for others. In reality it's to help you get through this man. Nobody is perfect. It wasn't meant to be. Own it and move on.-"

Smiling through my tears I know he is being honest with me. This is the same guy who has been there for me since seventh grade.

"-You're an ass, but I guess I am the real ass. I'll take responsibility.-"

I hop in the shower still spewing out water from my eyes. Memories terrorizing me. What I could have done, should've done, should not have done. Hunched against the shower wall I beg, "Oh God. Help me feel better. I don't want to feel like this. Why do I feel this way still?" I'm pounding on the shower wall with the bottom of my closed fist because I destroyed my knuckles hitting concrete. Standing in the shower stall with my head hanging, the water falls down my back, swirling in the drain for a good twenty-five minutes. Once showered, I step out of the stall and dry off with the last clean towel available.

Attempting to get dressed and get myself together, I end up in shambles, leaning back against the kitchen wall and making another emergency call to W.

"What up dog? How ya' doing?"

"H…h…hey." I manage to squeak out.

"Yo! Whats wrong? You O.K.?"

I'm struggling to breath and howl, "Um, No, I'm not alright. It's all ma…ma…my fault man."

"Yo man. Get yourself together. It's not all your fault. It takes two bro. Remember, I asked you if you would be ready for this. You said you thought you would."

"I thought…thought I would be. I didn't think it would be…be… be this soon."

"Mayi it didn't work when you were there giving it your all. Think about it. What would it be like if you went back? Nothing has changed. You guys would still be fighting. She wasn't even who you thought she was anyway. Hiding boyfriends, her feelings. Fuck. According to the divorce papers she even lied to you about her income!"

"Bro, I feel used. Paying and working my butt off for her and her kids and meanwhile she is making more bank than me. Her keeping me around for help as needed when she had a boyfriend. You're right. I wouldn't go back. I was nasty though."

"I'm sure you both were. There is no love in war! Get it together. You're happy at the apartment. You got your kid. You're playing ball. Get this over with and move on. You got plenty of girls to date. This is your sign that it is time to totally move on."

"Damn! You're right bro. I…uh am gonna finish this chapter and head to church. Then, my pops for dinner."

"Alright bro. Holler at me if you need anything. Dale!"

"Dale bro! Thank you, man."

God and the Universe have a funny way of speaking to you and Matthew 25: 41-46, could have cost me my life many times, but always gave me wisdom.

My Rock-Goon, Mayi, Los, Jax, Yes

BUT GOD

By early fall my emotions are in check (for the most part) and on-line church, writing, and driving, get me through. Spending time with lifelong friends and family helps. Meeting a few new friends helps, too. Feeling blessed and humbled by the journey, I practice patience and kindness to myself and others.

The morning of October 7th a text pings from Veronica, a new girl I have been talking to for a bit. *"-Hey. If you know someone who needs a roommate, I kinda just got kicked out of my place. Got in a fight with my roommate. Help!-"*

That verse, Matthew 25:43. That verse that I just haven't been able to stop thinking about since accepting that my marriage was over. *"Would I provide food, shelter, and cloth someone in need? Hadn't I helped Suzy? Here the Lord is giving me a chance to put my faith to the test. I don't know this chick very well though, but shit, I didn't know Suzy at all. Just do it. You know you can't turn down a damsel in distress. Maybe that's my problem though."*

I pull into a gas station on Lantana Road and sit staring at my phone, contemplating whether I am prepared to invite anyone into my home, let alone a woman. Taking a huge breath of air into my lungs I unlock my phone, hope for the best, and dial. *"Maybe she won't answer, and we can say we tried."* On the fourth ring she answers.

Letting my breath out with each word. "Heeey. Veronica, how are you doing?"

"Well, I've had better days."

"Yeah. I see that. Veronica, I need to ask you a question. Do you do any drugs?"

"I smoke weed."

"Yeah, no worries. Everyone smokes weed. I'm not sure that's really a drug. Do you do any other drugs?"

"The only drugs I have are what's prescribed to me. One for my PTSD, one to sleep, one for seizures, one for anxiety. Sorry, it's embarrassing, but I don't need them all the time."

I have no experience with prescription drugs, but for some reason I think, *"A little weed. No big deal. She probably has some issues, but this is temporary. We all have issues. I can give her a safe environment for a little while."*

"As long as you don't do them all at once, girl. Veronica, I'm going to do you a solid. Giving you the deal of a lifetime. You can stay at my place until December. After that, I move out and can't take you with me. You don't have to pay me a dollar. Not for rent, not for food. I can take care of my own bills. In exchange, please save all your money and be ready to go on your own when the time comes. I'm not gonna make any moves on you. That is not what this offer is about. I am a devoted Christian. I want to make this clear. I have an opportunity to help and want to."

"Umm…uh…ah…I don't know what to say."

"Well, you think about it and let me know."

"I'm flattered. I'll pay you. I just got a job."

"It would serve us better if you just saved your money so you could move on when it's time to go. I won't be able to help you then."

"Thank you Mayi. Come get me. The address is 3838 Broadway Street., Lantana. I'll be ready. I really appreciate it."

"I'm not too far. I'll see you soon."

Redirecting my car towards Veronica's place in the muggy and wet roadways I turn off the apps. Once there, we load my car up in the drizzle, and navigate to my apartment. Halfway there, Veronica pulls down her mask and looks at me with her big blue eyes. "Xanax is prescribed for my anxiety. Is that an issue?"

I turn down the volume since the talk seems serious by her shaky tone. "It's prescribed right? You don't abuse it?"

"Yes, it is. I don't abuse it. Mayi…anything to keep a needle out of my arm, you feel me?"

"I get it. O.K." My stomach drops knowing the mantra. Never believe an addict. Regret, buyer's remorse, and worry set in deep, like I ate too much greasy bacon. *"What have I just gotten myself into? Fuck man. I asked if she did drugs, but guess I should've rephrased too 'ever' did? Damn. Don't judge though. Be nice."*

The next four weeks are bizarre. Veronica makes it to work only on Monday's and misses the rest of the week, all four weeks. I begin to wonder what type of job she actually landed. She left the old home without any underwear. I help her out and buy her some items at Victoria Secret on Moving Day. Within two weeks she is modeling them for me in bed. Lust has won again, and I feel like a fraud. I kept a wall up because of her troubled past and after a few times lost interest as I got to know her more.

Sitting on my couch week three, watching Netflix Veronica interrupts with her own commercial break, "Mayi I've been to prison for two years for selling drugs. The women in there are nasty. Worse than men."

"Really. It's that bad?" I scratch my head in concern and fear of what she will say next.

Tears fill her eyes. "Man, I've been gang raped, beat up and sold. My dad used to be my drug hookup. I've met some great friends down here though." She shows me her friends on Facebook.

"Wow. That's crazy man. I can't believe your dad was your hookup."

"Yeah, he's a scumbag. My stepmom was a hooker. He found her using and she hanged herself. Drapes are hung and people are hanged, ya know that? Hey, you think we could get my cat Bailey?"

"I can't have animals in here. Wish I could."

By November it is clear that Suzy and Veronica have more in common than I ever imagined. In the early morning hours, a scream wakes me.

"FUCK! DAMN! OWWW!"

I jump out of my bed and run to the living room. "Veronica, what happened? You O.K.?"

"I hit my head. I tripped and fell. Help me up please. OOWWW!" She slurs and turns around. I grab her hand, lift her up and look at my door.

"Dude, my door is wide open again! This is the third time this week!"

"Uh...uh...oh...wha-" Her right eye is drooping and the other is closed, her arms are moving disjointedly and don't match the step she attempts.

Grabbing her arm and moving her toward the couch, "Veronica you can hardly keep your balance. Sit down so you don't hurt yourself."

"Wha...wah you talking about? Yoooo duurs, door, is close."

"I just closed it! Go to bed, but tomorrow we need to talk. I can't keep living like this. You were supposed to get on your feet. You're not going to work. You're a liability leaving my door open. This is not the best area and I can't go to bed in peace with you here. I can't trust you."

Falling asleep in a heap in the corner, she screams "O.K.!" and falls back into the couch curled up like a pile of dirty laundry.

Pointing towards my bed, I yell, "Let's go! Bedtime! I have to be up early. Let's go!" Veronica stumbles along behind me and makes it onto the bed. I finally fall back to sleep on my couch after some tossing and turning. When I wake up the next morning and walk in my kitchen there are two powdery blue lines a few inches long on the white countertop.

I don't bother to wake Veronica up and leave for work. I take pictures of the blue powder lines and wash them into the sink. Getting in my car, I send the pictures to "W" and call him before driving.

"W" is 6'4, with just as tall a resume of bad ex's, one even tried to stab him years ago. "Yo W. I woke up to two blue powder lines man."

"What? Mayi you gotta do something bro. You have a kid. You can't have that man."

"I know. I don't know what to do bro. I want to help this chick, but man she left the door open again last night." I laugh. "Bro she busted her ass again on her face this time."

"Duuuude…sorry Mayi but she has to go man. She's too erratic. The other day she was in the garbage can with her stuff."

"I know man. I just want to keep my word."

"Then deal with it, but don't bother me with this again. Let me know what happens. Gotta go."

"Later."

All day this decision weighs on me. When I park, I pray. "Dear Lord, thank you for this wonderful day. Lord, in the name of Jesus Christ, I pray that you forgive me for my earthly sins. I pray you give me the right words for Veronica and help me with whatever we discuss. In the name of Jesus Christ I pray, Amen."

I walk in and realize the Lord answered my prayer. There is no sign of Veronica in the little apartment. Calling W's phone as I look under my bed, just to be certain, he picks up.

"Yo W, she's not here."

"Whaaaaat? She's not there. Problem solved and you didn't have to do anything."

"Yeah, I guess man. Oh shit." I see her nightstand is packed with pill bottles. "Well, it won't be for long. She left her eight pill bottles here and her clothes."

"Mayi, maybe she's looking for a place to stay."

"I've told her the best place for her is with her mom. I told her she should go back to Pennsylvania. No place better than home you know."

"Mayi some people just don't know a good thing. You gave her a huge hand-up. Nothing you should feel bad about."

"Yo bro, since I don't have to babysit at my place anymore, let's go out tomorrow."

"Dale. Talk tomorrow."

"Later."

I change into boxers and a tank top after my shower. For the first time in weeks, I sleep like a baby. The next afternoon, Happy Hour is spent with Yez, Ricky, my cousin Ryan and W at Max's Grille in Mizner Park. Been coming to this spot for years in downtown Boca. Tons of pretty ladies with smiles hidden behind face masks. Luxury cars cruising the circle. People are loosely adhering to the government COVID-19 mandates. Governor De Santis is not having any more lockdown and the state of Florida is considered a "hot zone." That term is correct in every way.

After Mizner we walk a few blocks to the sports bar, "The Standard." The new bar offered full menus to adhere to the COVID-19 ordinances. Bars without food service could not be open, yet restaurants could. I thought alcohol or drinking a little bleach killed anything, but the CDC did not agree with that.

We head straight for the bartender behind the long oak bar with blue lights shining underneath. Ryan says, "What you want Mayi and W? I got this round."

W responds, "I'll have a Rum and Coke and I'll take care of the next round."

"I'll take a Yuengling. Thank you, guys, because I'm broke as a joke. Divorces are costly. Can't wait for it to be over soon."

Ryan hands us our drinks, tips the bartender cash and says, "Leave the tab open." Hip-hop music is jamming. We head to the outside high-top table, where it's a little quieter. Ryan sits down on a bar stool and immediately begins to entertain a pretty brunette sitting to his right. W and I post up alongside the table, both ready to be his wing man as needed, and chat.

"Veronica was not at my apartment today either, bro. I have no clue where she's at."

W sips his rum and coke slowly. We are so close I can hear his ice cubes clash against his glass. "Hey, don't question it bro. It's like you say. Everything happens for a reason. You did what you could."

The broad Ryan is talking to makes eye contact with me three times and I notice her teal colored-eyes. On the third time we lock eyes, I walk over to her left side, extend my hand, and introduce my-self. "Hey, I'm Mayi. Nice to meet you."

She warmly shakes my hand back and with a huge smile showing her bright pearly whites, says, "Hi, I'm Lilly. Nice to meet you, too." I return to W's side, not saying another word to Lilly all night. While she was intriguing, it would not be right to step on my cousin's toes.

At the end of the night, Ryan is still macking it to Lilly in the park-ing lot well after last call. I stand next to her and make eye contact with Ryan while W and I wait patiently.

"Time to go home Ryan?" I ask.

Ignoring me, fixated on Lilly, Ryan cajoles, "Lilly you coming to hang out or what? Come on. Let's go back to my house or your bal-cony to smoke."

Lilly doesn't answer right away, looking around as though she is searching for something, or someone. She suddenly turns and points her hot-pink painted finger directly at my face and declares, "Hmmmm, well…if I'm going to hang out with anyone tonight it's going to be with him."

I turn around, looking to my left and right, then behind me, but I'm the only one there. Making eye contact with Ryan, looking for an answer from him, trying not to crack a smile, because I don't know what to say. Never wanting to be a cock blocker, but excited by the turn of events, Ryan answers before I can come up with anything cool to say, "Ohhhh, cool. You two hang out. Come on. I'll take you guys to Mayi's car at Max's."

Still in shock I wrap my arm around Lilly and smile. "Hi!"

She smiles back, tilts her head demurely to lean into my shoulder and seems a little shy after acting so brazen. "Hi." She giggles. "Wasn't sure how this was gonna work out. Glad you said yes."

Lilly and I hang out that night and the rest of the weekend. We have deep conversation about divorce, children, accomplishments, and goals. We watch the Sunday NFL games, including the Miami Dolphin and Pittsburgh Steelers. She is a Pittsburgh girl. We agree to only root against each other when the two teams meet. Ironically, I realize Lilly and Veronica are both from Pittsburgh.

Sunday, before dropping her off, I perform what would be a life altering act. I ask her out on an official date. "Hey, you want to go on a date tomorrow evening? Nothing big. Maybe a hot chocolate or something? I know you don't like coffee."

She brushes her dark, long hair back and quickly answers. "Sure. I think I'd like that." I come around to the passenger side and open the door for her. She latches onto my shoulders and steals a kiss. As I pull out of her parking lot the feeling of her lips on mine lingers pleasantly.

Within a few minutes the deluge that the weatherman predicted attacks. The storm is whipping palm tree branches and the streets are slippery. Rather than trying to drive an hour away, I call Ricky.

"Yo, let me sleep over tonight. I don't want to drive home in this weather."

"I'm here. Come over."

"Awesome! Be there in five. I'm down the street."

Parking at "The Heritage" on 4th and Palmetto Park Road a text chimes in from Veronica. *"-Please I feel like I'm dying. Please. I need to get out of here.-"*

I text her back. *"-I wish I could help. I'm in Boca and no way I'm driving in this weather. There are severe flood alerts tonight. I hope you stay safe and find a way to fight through the night.-"*

Monday, November 16th, 2020, forever changes me. I rise at 5 A.M. The storm has passed leaving behind flooded roadways. Not many drivers are working, the money is good, but the day is treacherous. There are a few times I'm forced to abandon a call with no way to make it through some of the worst flooded areas. Making waves through the roads, feeling more like a boat captain than a car driver, I am relieved and weirded out to receive a text from Veronica at 7:48 A.M. She survived the night, but she never woke up early, for any reason.

"-Hey. You promised today. I really need to talk to you. I need help. I need to shower and figure out what I'm gonna do. Probably go back to work and a halfway house. I need to get my meds from your apartment so I can make this sale so I can use that money for a halfway house.-"

I pull into a nearby park in Ft. Lauderdale and answer her. *"-In Ft. Lauderdale. Will help you today and get you all your stuff when done working.-"*

At 9:37 A.M. my phone chimes. - *"It's been over an hour. PLEASE IM GONNA LOSE THIS SALE. I SENT YOU MY LOCATION. PLEASE BRING ME MY MEDS. PLEASE! Mayi please. Like I'm begging you. I'm freaking out. This kid is gonna go somewhere else. I need them now. PLEASE CALL ME.-"*

I'm in Deerfield Beach on 10th Avenue next to I-95, pulling into the Exxon so I can text safely and respond. *"-I understand. However, I have bills. I have a life, a job and responsibilities. I don't sleep all day and sell drugs getting screwed up all night, so I need you to wait. I have to take care of my bills and money first. I'm sorry but I'll be heading up soon. Very soon.-"*

Inside the station, grabbing a Laffy Taffy and a can of coke, she chimes in again. *"-You told me 2 hours ago. I'm sorry but I have no cigarettes, no nothing. I'm LOSING MY MIND. WHAT DID I DO TO DESERVE THIS. I KNOW YOU HAVE A LIFE. I CANT STAY HERE. I'M ABOUT TO BE ON THE STREET. I'm begging you Mayi please. I need this money to get in a halfway house and you're gonna screw it up. Please just work with me. This is not a safe situation and I need to get out of here.-"*

My conscience gets the best of me and I leave for West Palm Beach. Driving I say into the speaker of the car, "O.K. google. Text Veronica"- Leaving now. On my way up."

"Text Veronica leaving now. On my way up. Send it or cancel it?"

"Send it!"

Driving up the highway I distinctly remember the white "4-1-1 PAIN" billboards with pink stripes on the top and the bottom, depicting a pink car crashed into the center. I don't know why, but I counted five of those signs along the way. Veronica chimes, *"-Thank you. 5555 Haverhill Road.-"*

I call Veronica once I get off on 45th St. "Hey, where do you want me to pick you up?"

"At the gas station on Haverhill and 45th St. please."

Veronica is waiting outside. She is wearing the same black sweats and shirt I saw her in five days ago. She has not brushed her hair and smells almost moldy.

"Veronica, how are you? What the hell is going on?"

"Thank you for getting me Mayi. I needed to get out of there or I was going to die. Look, I just want to take a shower and have a few days to figure my crap out." She opens the door and sits down.

"O.K. You can stay one week, but you need to figure it out. I think you should go back home with your mom. No one is going to take care of you like your mom."

She lowers the passenger seat back all the way. "You think so? You really think that's what I should do?"

"I really do mama. That's your best move. I've gone back to my parents before. It may help. You're only thirty. You have your whole life ahead of you."

I look at her to see signs that she is high, but I can't tell. No one will ever know except for her and God, but it was extremely odd that she was up so early, more likely, she never went to sleep.

"You think you can drop me off at the gas station next to your house so I can do this deal and then I'll walk over?"

"Yeah, I guess. Just leave me out of that. I'll leave the door unlocked because I'm exhausted from all the driving. Just walk in. Remember to close it this time."

"Bet!"

Heading home after dropping her off, I keep shaking my head in disbelief at the current events until my exhaustion pulls me to the couch and sleep. The sound of Veronica scrubbing the shower and bitching at a stain on the tile wake me a few hours later. She is on her hands and knees with a bucket of water and yellow gloves on, sweating, "Dammit, you have no Lysol or anything? I'm having to use dish soap."

"Veronica, you don't have to do that. It's not easy to come by Lysol, or any cleaning products right now. Please get up. Have you showered yet?"

She stands up. "No, I haven't. Trying to get it clean first. I need to make it clean."

Turning on the water, "I think you should shower. You did a good job with what you had. I'll go second and then leave for work. You go first."

"O.K. thank you." Veronica brushes up against my chest and turns to hug me, but I make it clear.

"I just want to help you. I don't want to be intimate. We are just friends and that's it. I can't live this crazy life. You need help."

She moves past me to close the door of the bathroom and says, "I'm sorry. Thank you for being so nice. I'll be out in a few minutes."

I yell through the door, "Keep the water running! I'll hop in after you."

"O.K!"

Veronica steps out twenty minutes later. "Hey, there is no more hot water. I'm sorry."

"It's ok. I gotta go anyway."

Grabbing my clothes in a pile, walking out my front door, and almost making it to the car, I am forced to stop when I feel a tug on the back collar of my t-shirt. Veronica is standing there holding her yellow EBT card.

"Please get me Red Bull and cigarettes on your way back."

"I got you."

Needing some sense of normalcy, I call Lilly. "Hi. How are you?"

"I'm good and yourself?"

"Not too bad. We still on for tonight? If you want, I can come now, and we can make it an early evening."

"Yeah, that will work better anyway."

I step on the gas pedal to arrive quicker as she says, "Come now."

"I'm hopping on I-95 now. I'll be in Boca in forty minutes. 5:15 to be safe."

"Cool. See you soon, bye."

"Bye."

The storm earlier has brought about a cold front. I drop the windows to feel the breeze, excited to see Lilly, but worried for Veronica. I have Lecrae, "I'll cry for your Heart" playing and a few other Christian songs I recently discovered follow it. I pick up Lilly and we go for hot chocolate at Starbucks in Mizner Park. We sit at the south end on a bench in the grassy knoll where they have begun to build the town's Christmas Tree. Caressing her cheek, I whisper, "You have beautiful light eyes." She smiles. "I love your smile. You are beautiful."

"Aww..." Her cheeks dimple, "Thanks Mayi."

"You are beautiful inside and out. I can feel how genuine you are." I brush her hair behind her ear. She displays her full-watt smile. We kiss, talk, kiss some more, and talk for hours.

At the end of the night with Lilly, before leaving Mizner Park, I look her in her sparkling eyes and confess. "I have to come clean. There is this girl I have been trying to help get sober staying at my apartment." Lilly pulls back from my arms. "I want you to know there is nothing there. She needs to figure it out, but I don't want to put her on the street. I think she's going to be going to a halfway house or home to Pennsylvania within a week. That's the deadline I gave her."

"Geez! That's a lot for a first date." Lilly covers her mouth with her hands and slides to the edge of the green bench, moving away from me. "Does she know you're here with me?"

"No way. I would never do that. She is fragile. I have been fighting myself about telling you all night, but since we have been so honest about everything, I didn't want to lie to you. Not even by omission."

"I choose to believe you. That is not something easy to come clean about. You also didn't have to tell me. I see how kind you are to me and others." She turns toward me, but still keeps her distance and continues, "However. This is a cardinal rule with me. You get three dramas. You know your baseball. Three strikes and you're out! I'm out. You're on strike one." We both laugh and I reach toward her to grab her hand and pull her close. She is shivering a bit while I caress her shoulder and her neck. "Let's get out of here. It's really getting cold, and I'm not dressed for it."

I kiss her and then look at my watch. "Lilly it's almost 9:30. I have to drop you off, then still ride to Veronica. She is supposed to be at my apartment, but who knows." I look back up at her. "Can I see you tomorrow?"

"Yes. I like the way you make me feel. I enjoy spending time with you. We all have a past. Yours is just more recent."

She grabs my elbow, and we walk arm-in arm to the car, strolling like the old couples I envy. "Good. I really enjoy hanging out with you. You're such a cool, and sweet woman. I love your eyes and smile. You watch football, you cook. I could go on."

"Awwww."

"Come on. Let's get out of here."

After dropping off Lilly down the street and heading back up north on the highway, exhaustion hits me. When I open my front door (that is actually shut for once) a mess of mail greets me. Grabbing the envelopes and flyers with two hands I drop them on the coffee table with the other unopened notices. Scanning the apartment, I see Veronica passed out on my bed with her knees on the floor and her arms stretched out next to her in blue sweatpants and a purple windbreaker. I choose not to bother her and sit to text Lilly from my couch. We communicate briskly from 10:22 P.M. until 11:08 P.M. It is then I decide to check on Veronica again.

"Veronica! Wake up girl. Veronica." Making my way over to the bed from the living room, I think, *"Odd, she is usually up at this time."* Veronica's calf is sticking out from my view in the hallway. Her normally pale, white skin is way darker than I recall, almost maroon. "Veronica? Yo! You alright?" Panicking by the time I reach her; I yell and nudge her on the side twice. Her face looks normal on its side. "Veronica! Oh God! NO!" Veronica never answers and when I touch her face the other side turns to look at me, lopsided, as if a stroke occurred. The top half is pail. The bottom half that was compressed against the bed is brown, red, and purple. I run back to the living room, recoiling from her body, and struggle to dial my phone or even unlock it, my hands shaking. I finally hit the right digits, 9-1-1.

"Hello, Operator. What's your emergency?"

"I believe I have a possible overdose here."

"Are they breathing?"

"NO!"

"I need you to give me your address and then we are going to administer CPR." I comply. "O.K. I have dispatched Palm Springs fire rescue and police. Sir, I need you to place them flat on the ground so we can administer CPR."

"O.K. I already have her on her back."

"Sir, below the chest I need you to compress."

"Yes, I learned this in high school. Around the sternum." I place my right palm just under the sternum and grab it with my left and begin compressions.

"Sir, are you compressing? I don't hear you. Count out in 5's with me."

"And 1- and 2-and 3-and 4-and 5." Each time I would compress, the sound of an open wind tunnel howled back at me in evil laughter, "Woosh, woosh, woosh, woosh."

"DAMN IT VERONICA! COME BACK! PLEASE COME BACK!"

After the third futile attempt the Operator asks me to grab her wrist. "Dude she's dead man. She has no pulse. She's not here." I drop Veronica's limp wrist and run my hand up my forehead and through my hair trying not to cry. For the first time in my life, I witnessed death. Her eight pill bottles are open and scattered across the other side of the bed all over the floor. The only witness to her passing.

"Sir do you want to keep performing CPR? Want to perform with me until help gets there?" The sound of sirens nearby fills the air. Red and blue lights start shining through the cracks in my blinds.

"They are here man. I'm going to let them in."

"O.K. sir. I will let you talk with them."

"Thank you for your help." I hang up the phone and rush to open the door.

First responder asks, "Where are they?"

"In my room." I lead the procession of police, firemen, and EMT's into the house, not noticing who's who at this point. A fireman leads me into my living room. Then, policeman #1 leads me outside. Policeman #2, tall, stocky and brown, approaches one minute later, blocking my door. I try to go back inside and policeman #2 doesn't let me.

"You can't go back in there, sir. This is a crime scene." Policeman #2 firmly states.

"A crime scene? Man, this is an overdose. Simple. Can I at least grab a few things?"

"Sorry sir. I said you can't go back in there until the detective gets here and that's if he allows it."

Hot, tired, and in shock, I raise my voice. "You know you could have told me to get my phone before bringing me outside."

Policeman #2 states, "You were already outside."

I bark back, "Yes, because your buddy over there walked me out."

By 2:00 AM the detective has not arrived at the scene. "Officers if you need me, I'll be in my car sleeping. I have been up since 5 A.M. driving. Wake me when the detective gets here." I step in the passenger front seat and adjust it as far back as possible. Tossing and turning to get comfortable, I fall asleep, but it's a short nap.

Hearing, "Tap, Tap, Tap," on my passenger side window glass, I open the door and step out to a towering fellow in khakis and a black collared shirt. Had to be about 6'5 with a buzz cut and a thick Southern drawl.

I'm still upset and jump out of the car. "What time is it man?"

In his southern twang. "Mayi it is 3:30 in the morning. Sorry to keep you waiting so long. I'm Detective Chevy Shackles. I understand there are some items you need to get in there. A phone and laptop they said."

Detective Chevy Shackles points at me. "Follow me to my squad car please."

I comply. "Yes sir."

Once in the car detective Shackles reads my Miranda Rights and takes my statement.

"For the record repeat your name and address please."

"Mayi. Palm Springs."

"In your own words what happened here today?"

"To the best of my knowledge I left here around 3:30 P.M. Veronica was still alive. I went on a date with a girl named Lilly in Boca. When I got home at about 10:15 Veronica was already dead, I guess, and I didn't realize it. From what I know of her, I would suspect it was a drug overdose."

"What makes you suspect a drug overdose?"

"Well, sir, she was a drug addict. I believe she was back on heroin. Though she would not admit that to me. When you check the scene thoroughly, you're going to see her pill bottles. I left them all there exactly where they were. I haven't touched anything other than giving CPR."

"Did she know you were on this date?"

"No sir. She was not here for the last five days and I picked her up today. While we were not in a relationship, I didn't want to upset her either. I was trying to help her get clean and sober."

"Do you know where she was?"

"I know the address, but I have no clue who is there, or why she was there, 5555 Haverhill Road."

He grabs a form from his file folder and says, "Alright, that's all I need as far as a statement. If you can sign this here it gives us permission to search your residence and collect whatever we feel we need to solve this and rule out foul play. You know, just doing our job and due diligence. When we are done, you can go back in there."

"No problem. Here you go."

"Thank you Mayi. We will be done here in about thirty minutes and be on our way. You can wait in your car or outside."

"Thank you, sir." I walk to my passenger front seat and fall asleep until they are done.

Finally, being allowed back in, the mess is out of control, and the home appeared ransacked. I grab my phone and reach out to Veronica's best friend on social media, not knowing who else to contact or how to reach anyone. She immediately responds to my message that Veronica has passed away. *"-This is her mom's number. Please call her. I let her know you would be calling, but didn't tell her Veronica is dead. I just can't. I can't believe this. Is this real?-"*

"-I'm sorry. It is.-"

Calling Veronica's Mom was the hardest thing I have ever had to do in my entire life. The whole incident feels like a nightmare.

"Ma'am this is Mayi. I'm sorry and I don't know how to tell you this." My words slow and it's like I'm watching someone else say them.

A primal screech escapes her, "NOOOoooo! Tell me it's not true."

"Ma'am Veronica passed last night. I'm sorry. I tried."

"WHY? WHA…Wha…whyyyy? Not my baby. Please don't tell me my baby!"

I break down and can hardly muster out, "I…I…I…I'm…I'm so…so…sorry. I failed."

"I'm going to let you go. It's not your fault. She said very nice things about you. She was sick and troubled. Thank you for trying to help her. I guess I always knew this day would come." The phone clicks and the finality causes me to cry even harder.

I throw my phone and cover my face. My convulsions hurt. I lay down and try to sleep unsuccessfully. I decide to call W at 5:30 in the morning.

"Hey Mayi. What's wrong with you man?"

"EH…UH…AH…She…She…Sh…EH…AH…She died. She di…died last night man."

"Who man? Veronica?"

"Yeah…waaa…waaa…"

"Yo man! Get yourself together. There was nothing you could do. It was bound to happen. We both know that, but I'm sorry to hear that man. No one deserves that. She was troubled. At least she's not in pain anymore."

I stand up and pace. "Bro she…sh…she overdosed in my apartment."

"Aw man, no way. I'm sorry to hear that Mayi. You found her huh?"

"Yeah man. When I got home from hanging out with Lilly. Oh man, that makes her my alibi." I smack myself in the head. "What a way to start a relationship. Shit. Bro, I'll never forget Veronica's face. I was the last one to see her alive and the one to find her dead. I just keep seeing her two faces. The one alive and the dead one. It's terrible."

"Aw dude, I'm sorry man. You can come over if you want."

"I think I will man. I haven't slept and I can tell my body isn't going to bed anytime soon. Thank you, bro. Later."

"It ain't your fault bro. You did what you could. Later."

Leaving for Boca, I grab a Red Bull and land at Jaxson's house. Stepping in I do the normal routine and stand with my hands out and turn while he sprays me with the disinfectant of the day. Once clean, I take off my mask and sit down out on the deck in a plastic folding chair. He sees me more vulnerable than he has ever seen me in his life. He sits down next to me silently while I look through text messages with my puffy eyes.

"Maaayiiii. Don't. Don't do that to yourself."

"I'm sorry bro. I can't. What if I didn't leave yesterday? What if I make it home earlier? Rereading these text messages, I can see just how unstable she was. Should've checked her in somewhere, or called her Mom. It's my fault man. I might have been able to save her."

Jaxson sits next to me on his leather couch. "No Mayi. You would have watched her die man, trying to save her. You would have been there. God didn't want you to see that happen. Maybe you would have been able to save her, or maybe she dies in your arm. It's a blessing you weren't there."

Covering my face with both my hands, "EH...EH...AH...AH... EE...WA...EE...WA" I continue to sob. He hands me some napkins off the table to wipe my face. I stand up, "Yo man thanks for letting me come by. I love you bro. I gotta go."

Jaxson stands up. "Mayi stay a while longer."

"Nah bro. I really gotta go."

Jaxson walks to the kitchen, grabs an orange from the fruit bowl on the counter and hurls it at me. "At least have an orange!"

I catch it swiflty,hard against my palm, just like when we were kids."O.K. I'll take it for the road, jackass." I swing by W's house to relax there for a few hours before returning home. Sitting on his brown leather couch we go over the recent events.

"W, there is a God. I have been thinking how lucky I am she was next to my bed. If she is anywhere else, she falls and hits her head on the tile and I'm a murder suspect."

"Holy shit! I didn't think of that Mayi. You are lucky my friend. Stop putting yourself in those situations. You need to focus on you and your son. Do you have Lysol?"

"Lysol for what bro? I can't find any on the shelves. That's one of the last things Veronica brought up to me."

"Well…" He rubs his chin. "I know the Lysol warning label says it kills COVID-19. Does it clean death? If it does, spray your bed sheets where she fell."

"You're such a dick bro. Cracking jokes at a time like this. I'm buying new sheets."

W laughs. "I'm serious man."

Leaving W's, I cancel with Lilly. The week is spent praying and crying. Guilty feelings of not being there to be able to try and save Veronica overwhelm me at times. Her face haunts me. It's impossible to focus on work. Detective Shackles harasses me.

"You mind giving us your phone?"

"What do you need my phone for in an overdose case?"

"We just want to rule you out."

"I'll wait on the Tox report and Autopsy. I'll take my chances. You know where I am."

Lilly cheers me up at the end of the days. Some days are easier than others and I make it to Saturday, November 21st. I wake up and throw on my Christian music, skipping the morning work split and rest. I drop my white towel after the shower, change into blue jeans and a t-shirt. Veronica's twin sister is on her way to grab her belongings.

"KNOCK…KNOCK…KNOCK!"

"Come in."

"Hi, I'm Valerie. I came for the rest of my sister's stuff." I am staring at the spitting image of a dead girl.

"Hi. I'm truly sorry about your loss. I really tried." She shrugs her shoulders and doesn't say much, thankfully. Even her voice has the same ring as Veronica's.

She leaves. I need to get to church to shake this feeling of darkness. Pulling up to church, there are newly established checkpoints set up for social distancing. At the first checkpoint a heavyset redheaded woman takes my temperature while wearing gloves and double-masks. The next, a man in blue glasses and a matching pullover performs a Covid questionnaire with me. He hums to my answers, checking boxes off one by one.

"Sir, have you traveled outside of Florida in the last fourteen days?"

"No."

"Do you know if you have been exposed or around anyone who has been exposed to COVID-19?"

"No."

"Have you been experiencing any dry cough, fever, aches, pains or loss of taste?"

"Nope!"

"Thank you, sir. You may proceed." He moves out of my way, allowing me to drive into the parking lot and toward the field behind the church.

Volunteers are still setting up the bandstand. My Honda is third in the row, right to left. A small group is gathered under a blue tent in the distance. Most people remain in their car or sit around in grouped lawn chairs, denoting families that live together. Only once in your group, you may take your mask off. I see Edward and Conny, but don't wave because they are turned away from me. Taking a deep breath and slouching in my seat, I get comfortable, ready to feel the peace wash over me that only Jesus can bring me. Looking around, I admire happy families and cars full of people gather in the name of the Lord.

These visits were one of the few times a week where I saw multiple people at once. Visits with the outside world had become strange. Across the country, robberies were on the rise. Domestic violence increased. Suicide increased. Depression rates increased. Unemployment was at its highest in decades.

A vaccine for COVID-19 was in the works. That is what citizens continued to be told by every politician from across the globe. A vaccine race between various pharmaceutical companies, and countries, was mid-war. Conspiracy theories abounded from Wuhan scientists purposely releasing the virus, to our own President being involved. Church was my time to let all the questions and burdens of life go.

Pastor Chris began to preach, "In our culture today there is so much division, so much happening. Some people feel it justifies them in their sin, anger, and cruelty. They may question people of God. They may not believe. Are you one of them? Are you justifying the way you feel, the way you post on social media, in anger? Are you one of them? Or are you taking counsel from people that react to life's challenges in anger or hate? Who are you getting counsel from? Jacob says, my soul will not enter any of their counsel." He walks around the stage looking into car windshields at faces too far away to identify positively.

"James says this in chapter 1, verses 12-15 in the new living translation; God blesses those who patiently endure testing and temptation. Afterwards they will receive the crown of life that God has promised to those who love Him and remember when you are being tempted do not say, God is tempting me. God never leads anyone into temptation.

Temptation is the work of Satan and comes from our own desires, our own egos, which entice us and drag us away from the word. These desires give birth to sinful actions and when sin is fed it grows, eventually giving birth to death. If anyone should recognize sin or anger, it is God's children. He doesn't call us to sin. He doesn't call us to anger. If we decide to live a life of sin, or anger, James is saying our lives will be unstable and our destiny unfulfilled. We will not excel."

"I say again show me your decisions, show me how you lead, how you follow, and I'll show you your destiny. What decisions are you making today? With all that is going on, with all that you see." Pastor Chris walks back to the podium and flips the page.

"James goes on in verse 8-12. Here is where the good news arrives. Sometimes it's hard to preach a message when you're saying, man, you really gotta check your heart! Nowadays we say, check yourself before you wreck yourself." The crowd laughs. "If anyone knows the Holy Spirit can do work in our hearts, it's us." He smiles and looks around at the rows of cars, five deep now.

"He says in Judas's verse 8; you are he whom your brothers shall praise. Your hand shall be on the neck of your enemies. Your father's children shall bow down before you, verse 9 of Genesis 49, the scepter shall not depart from Juda nor a lord giver from between his feet until Shiloh comes." Pastor Chris voice begins to ascend louder and louder. "To him shall be the obedience of the people, binding his donkey to the vine and his donkey's coal to the choice vine. He washes garments in wine and his clothe in the blood of grapes. His eyes are darker than wine and his teeth whiter than milk." He pauses for a moment and begins again with a caring tone.

"The good news is simple. Once you choose goodness, life is blessed. The best response to a problem is prayer. When you're feeling unloved you can praise God. When things are not going your way, you can praise God. Anytime, anywhere. No one can rob you of your opportunity to spend time with the Lord."

His words bring me back to Veronica's death. "*I can only control my actions and no one else's. I need to practice being more forgiving. All those moments with Veronica were results of choices I made. Sleeping with her was wrong. I definitely gave into temptation. Trying to help her stop using was not. Maybe it didn't work out, but I had to try. Lord, you have shown me where I can do better, and where I did my best. I really like Lilly. I don't want to make any more mistakes. Please forgive my sins and give me the strength to grow. I am humbled by your message. It is received. Amen.*"

After service, feeling lighter on my feet and in my spirit, I approach Edward and Conny under the blue tent. We gather beside a flag-pole, proudly waving the American flag in the air.

"Hey guys. How are you?"

"Hey Mayi! How are you?" They both say.

"I'm great. What a service, huh?"

"It was a great message, wasn't it?" Ed says.

"It was. It's been a heck of week. Thank you for having me over for dinner last week. Salmon was great, Conny."

"You know you can count on us for anything. We love you bud. Keep praying. You will get through this tough time." Conny hugs me. Then, I give Ed a hug.

After helping them break down the tent, we say our goodbyes. I dart back to my car, hit the start button and head North to Royal Palm Beach. Christian music fills the car.

I arrive to the biggest house on the block.

"KNOCK...KNOCK...KNOCK!"

My dad opens the door and I immediately give him a hug. "Hi Papi!"

"Hi Papo. How are you?" He responds and turns to walk to the back of the house.

Following him to the backyard I chatter away. "Things are O.K. Papi. Going through a tough time, but we all are. I'll be O.K." We stand near the grill as the steaks sizzle away. "It's funny you invited me to eat today."

He flips a steak over and says, "Oh, why is that?"

"Papi, I've been crying all day. A lot of emotions running through me."

He flips the other steak and places both on dinner plates. "Steaks are ready. You wanna eat?"

The smell of charred meat and peppery spices fills my nose, my stomach grumbles and I'm actually excited to chew versus inhaling fast food here and there.

"Dad what are you going to do when you sell the house?" My mom and he were still in the middle of separating, at least as far as I knew.

"I haven't made up my mind."

"I'm moving back to Boca after the New Year. I can't wait to be back with the family down there. I'm always down in that town anyways. You should come."

"It's a thought."

We finish eating and chit-chat some more, laying on either side of the oversized couch. In usual fashion after a big meal, we pop on a movie and he falls asleep within ten minutes. I get up off the leather couch, throw a fluffy blue blanket over him, kiss him on the cheek, and take off.

The Championship game was rescheduled for tomorrow due to COVID-19. I get home and remove my shoes at the entry, remove my shirt at the bedroom door, throw my remaining clothes in the corner of the closet, and dive under the covers. The life of a bachelor. Before dozing off, I get in a quick prayer.

"Lord, thank you for everything you have given me and everything you haven't. Thank you for everyone you have brought in, and taken out, of my life. Thank you for this glorious day. I know each breath is a miracle. Please keep working on my heart and mind. Don't give up on me. I will never give up on you. Help me with my lustful ways. Help me be patient and graceful. Help me be more selfless. Thank you for opening my eyes to my imperfections. It hurt! You always find a way to speak to us. We just have to listen. I know no matter what happens today or tomorrow, your promise is kept. Protect those who need protection. Save those that need saving. In the name of Jesus Christ please forgive me for my earthly sins. Amen!"

Throughout the night, like a kid playing in his first high school game, I wake up in anticipation. When I can't sleep, I count baseballs. Beats counting sheep. This trick comes in handy a few times between my short cat naps over the course of the night. Despite not getting much shuteye, the adrenaline wakes me up feeling ready to win this thing. The heat index is ninety degrees with no rain forecast and clear skies. I rock the slingshot, jumping on I-95 and doing ninety mph the whole way.

I arrive at the field and to our full squad that looks like a who's who of retired MLB players. An old White Sox catcher hits a three-run bomb. An ex-Brave short stop follows with his own bomb, giving my team a 5-1 lead. The next inning our teenage phenom pitcher, who throws as fast as I drove the slingshot to the field, hits another homerun. We win the game 7-1.

Normally, I stay and have a few beers with my teammates, but this day I have to rush home. The slingshot whips up the scenic A1A coastline. The beaches are blocked off to visitors, but I can still enjoy looking at the waves through the open cockpit along the way. Due to limited travel across the world, and most people staying home, water pollution has decreased. The ocean is as clear as Bahamian shores, a neon blue almost. While driving, "Reason" by Unspoken starts to play through my earphones attached to my cell phone. My Slingshot doesn't have a radio. Singing to the words about "four seasons of winter" I become euphoric, feeling I have made it through four tough seasons with the help of family, friends, and God.

There is more tribulation ahead. COVID-19 has made life uncertain, for those who thought they had it all figured out, and for those that never had a plan at all. God is there for everyone. Sure, we will fail at times. We will want to give up at times. There will also be times of great joy. For all of the days, good and bad, I am grateful.

Made in the USA
Middletown, DE
06 February 2023

23476590R00146